A NOVEL BASED ON THE LIFE OF
FATHER MATTEO RICCI

DEFYING
DANGER

Nicole Gregory

THE
M
MENTORIS
PROJECT

Barbera Foundation, Inc.
P.O. Box 1019
Temple City, CA 91780

More information at www.mentorisproject.org

ISBN: 978-1-947431-23-2

Library of Congress Control Number: 2019932576

The Mentoris Project is a series of novels and biographies about the lives of great Italians and Italian-Americans: men and women who have changed history through their contributions as scientists, inventors, explorers, thinkers, and creators. The Barbera Foundation sponsors this series in the hope that, like a mentor, each book will inspire the reader to discover how she or he can make a positive contribution to society.

Contents

Foreword

First and foremost, Mentor was a person. We tend to think of the word *mentor* as a noun (a mentor) or a verb (to mentor), but there is a very human dimension embedded in the term. Mentor appears in Homer's *Odyssey* as the old friend entrusted to care for Odysseus's household and his son Telemachus during the Trojan War. When years pass and Telemachus sets out to search for his missing father, the goddess Athena assumes the form of Mentor to accompany him. The human being welcomes a human form for counsel. From its very origins, becoming a mentor is a transcendent act; it carries with it something of the holy.

The Barbera Foundation's Mentoris Project sets out on an Athena-like mission: We hope the books that form this series will be an inspiration to all those who are seekers, to those of the twenty-first century who are on their own odysseys, trying to find enduring principles that will guide them to a spiritual home. The stories that comprise the series are all deeply human. These books dramatize the lives of great Italians and Italian-Americans whose stories bridge the ancient and the modern, taking many forms, just as Athena did, but always holding up a light for those living today.

Whether in novel form or traditional biography, these

books plumb the individual characters of our heroes' journeys. The power of storytelling has always been to envelop the reader in a vivid and continuous dream, and to forge a link with the subject. Our goal is for that link to guide the reader home with a new inspiration.

What is a mentor? A guide, a moral compass, an inspiration. A friend who points you toward true north. We hope that the Mentoris Project will become that friend, and it will help us all transcend our daily lives with something that can only be called holy.

—Robert J. Barbera, President, Barbera Foundation
—Ken LaZebnik, Editor, The Mentoris Project

Chapter One

THE STRANGE FOREIGNER

It was a hot and humid summer morning in Nanking when the middle-aged peasant woman stepped out of the doorway of her small cottage with a pail full of water for her pigs. Glancing out onto the street, a sight caused her to stumble backward, dropping the bucket of water, which splashed across the cobblestones.

Her children and husband came running from the back of the house. In the street, her neighbors pointed to a shiny, bright red-and-blue sedan chair being carried by four strong men. They had been forced to stop because an ox in the street blocked them, refusing to move. The ox's owner—an old farmer from the country—shouted and pulled at the beast, then pulled out his whip and lashed it savagely, but still the ox would not move on the bumpy, mud-caked street.

The blue lacquered door of the sedan swung open, and down from it stepped a tall, thin man with golden brown eyes, a long thin nose, and high arched eyebrows. His beard was gray and white, yet he did not seem old. He wore a high black cap and a flowing robe of dark purple silk, around which was slung a pale blue sash. Peeking out from beneath the robe, the white tips of his silk shoes were covered with spots of mud.

"Do not whip the beast!" the tall man said in Mandarin, which caused the crowd to fall silent. It was as if a chicken had just talked! This strange foreigner, who wore the dress of a Confucian scholar, spoke their language perfectly. "Stand beside your animal, speak softly to it," he said, "and pull it gently alongside of you." As if he knew better than the farmer how to make the big animal move!

Dumbfounded, the old farmer did as the tall man suggested, and to the amazement of the crowd, the ox took a step, then another, and continued on its way.

The foreigner turned to scan the faces that were all fixed upon him, and smiled gently.

"May peace be upon you," he said, and climbed back up into the sedan and pulled the curtain next to his seat so that his face was hidden. The four carriers lifted the sedan and proceeded along the street, leaving the crowd staring after them.

"Who is that?" said the peasant woman to her neighbors.

"Li Madou . . . a religious man," said her husband. "He has another name, too . . . ." He struggled to remember how he'd heard it pronounced. "Matteo Ricci." He shook his head at the strange sound of the name.

"He's a foreigner—what is he doing here?"

"I've heard he can turn metal into silver."

"No, no, see his robes? He's a scholar."

The crowd continued to speculate with uneasiness about the strange tall man, then turned back to the tasks of the day.

Chapter Two

THE SOUL OF A JESUIT

Seven-year-old Matteo Ricci leaned his ear against the door of his parents' bedroom. They were arguing—and he heard them say his name.

"He can only tutor Matteo a few more weeks," his father, Giovanni, exclaimed. "He's joining the new religious order—the Jesuits!"

"We can find other tutors for the boy," said his mother, Giovanna, in a reassuring tone.

"Jesuits! I'm not sure what they stand for, but I don't like it. They call themselves the Society of Jesus—how arrogant! What about the Dominicans or Franciscans! Do they not follow Jesus too?"

"They do, my dear, but the Jesuits have a new spirit—their fervor for education and missionary work is waking up the church," said Giovanna. Then her voice dipped down a notch. "Matteo will have a very difficult time losing Bencivegni as a tutor. He likes him so."

His head tilted against the door, Matteo gulped. All the color drained from his face. His beloved tutor, the priest and teacher Niccolò Bencivegni . . . was leaving? The sting of tears filled his eyes and he turned away from the door.

His grandmother Laria was stirring in the rooms below in the Riccis' house, and Matteo slung his bag of books over his shoulder and went down to find her.

"Matteo, are you up so early?" she called out in a quiet voice.

"*Si, Nonna,*" replied the boy. He ran to where she sat in the large sitting room. He gently touched the silver cross that hung around her neck, admiring its intricate design and the way it shined. He loved his grandmother. And she made the most wonderful meat pastries in all of Italy.

Laria reached out to stroke his pale cheek and marveled at his narrow nose, high cheekbones, and thin dark eyebrows arched above his sensitive face. He was a quiet boy, but astute also. What was this sadness in his dark eyes?

"My boy," she said. "What has upset you?"

Matteo averted his eyes and would not answer.

Laria held on to his hand and said, "I know how much you enjoy your lessons, so study well today. And give my regards to Father Bencivegni. Take some sweet biscuits with you . . . ."

Matteo kissed his grandmother, scooped up two biscuits from the big table into his bag, then ran to the heavy wooden front door, pulled it open, and stepped into the golden morning sun that spilled over the red-tiled rooftops. He ran down the cool cobblestone street through the bucolic medieval town of Macerata, heading to the home of Bencivegni.

He paid no attention to the far-reaching view of rolling green valleys with olive trees and vineyards that opened up between side streets. He ran past the new clock tower that began to ring out at 8 a.m. on the hour. It featured small wise men bursting out of a tiny door to adore the baby Jesus—a peculiar mechanical clock that at any other time Matteo loved to watch. Now running along, he nearly bumped into a farmer pushing his cart of lemons, limes, and oranges into the square, and then he leaped over a tabby cat that darted in front of him.

Matteo had lived in this town since his birth on October 6, 1552, and knew the route to his tutor's house well. He flew past two rivers, the Potenza and the Chienti, which flowed by Macerata, but he took their natural beauty quite for granted. Located in the central part of Italy—not far from the Adriatic Sea to the east, in a region called the Marches, part of the Papal States—Macerata enjoyed a climate that was often warm and dry, the air fragrant with blooming citrus trees.

Matteo knocked on the door of his tutor's home, and when it opened, he looked up into the smiling face of the young priest and burst out, "Papa says you are leaving to become a Jesuit. Is this true? And why didn't you tell me?"

Bencivegni's smile vanished as he saw his distraught young pupil. He stepped aside and invited Matteo in.

"Matteo, let's go to our study and I will explain everything."

As usual, the young man showed the utmost respect for his pupil.

Once they were both seated in their chairs—Matteo's feet hardly reached the floor—Bencivegni began. "Yes, Matteo, this is true."

"But why?" the boy asked. "And what is a Jesuit?"

Matteo was not afraid to speak freely with his tutor. He loved this familiar room. He'd examined most of the books that lined one shelf and studied the maps of land and sea on the walls. Here he had learned the rudiments of mathematics, Latin, and even Greek. He'd learned the constellations of the stars, and about Italian painters, architects, and poets. His parents cared about his future, and his grandmother loved him, but she was uneducated. Only his tutor had captivated and challenged his young mind. A window at the side of the room overlooked a small courtyard where birds now splashed in a water fountain.

"Ah, let me explain," said Bencivegni, running a hand through his curly dark hair, thinking how to describe his decision to a seven-year-old.

The handsome good-natured priest had once been engaged to marry the daughter of a Macerata nobleman. Matteo knew this because he'd heard his parents talking about it. But then Bencivegni changed his mind about marrying because he'd experienced what townspeople said was a "calling" to become a priest. The young woman—and her father—had been really angry.

"The Jesuits are a new religious order, Matteo—that means they are a group of priests with a different way of living. I very much believe in everything they believe in, and so I want to join them."

"And what is so good about what they believe?" Matteo asked forthrightly.

Bencivegni looked at his pupil, who stared back at him with great earnestness and expectation.

"Just before you were born, Matteo, a Christian missionary from Spain named Francis Xavier wanted very much to show the people of China the virtues of becoming Christian. But he became sick and died before he could even try. He had already traveled very far—to Japan, in fact—to convert people there to Christianity. Because he believed that everyone should know the love and forgiveness offered by Jesus Christ."

He stopped, checking whether Matteo was following him,

and saw that indeed the boy was waiting for the next part of the story.

"I did not know Francis Xavier, but I've heard great stories about him," said Bencivegni. "He had once been a careless, frivolous young man. He was very intelligent and liked to have fun—he spent money without thinking. He was not always honorable with his friends, and he caused much trouble for his family. But he had made one friend named Ignatius from Loyola, Spain, who tried to get him to live as a Christian. Ignatius wanted Francis to lead a better life—to still have fun, of course, but to think more about his purpose, his Christian purpose, which is to help others."

Matteo listened, rapt.

"Soon Francis began thinking Ignatius was right—maybe his life could have more meaning if he thought about Jesus Christ and tried to be more like our Savior," Bencivegni continued. "Francis and Ignatius became friends, and then they made more friends and they all formed a small group who decided they wanted be the kind of Christians who travel the world and help very poor people and sick people. They begged for money to buy clothes and food for poor people, and they talked to people who did not even know about Christianity.

"And they all were very smart and they agreed that school had helped them learn about the world and to be brave and open-minded—and they wanted all children to have the chance to go to school."

"I think that is good," said Matteo. He understood that he had some connection to this story.

"So, a little less than twenty years ago, Ignatius, Francis Xavier, and their friends decided to call themselves the Society of Jesus, or Jesuits, and they believed in helping other people and in educating children. The pope gave them his blessing. And today many young men who agree with these ideas are joining the Society of Jesus, becoming what we call Jesuits. I want to be one of them, and so I will be leaving Macerata to go to Rome."

Silence followed, and Bencivegni watched Matteo take in this story. Though the boy was only seven, he grasped the meaning of his tutor's words and could even understand Bencivegni's decision.

"Well, when are you leaving?" Matteo asked, looking up again at the books on the shelf.

"Tomorrow. This will be our last lesson together. Now, shall we look at the Latin text?"

As Matteo reached to pull out his lesson book, he remembered the biscuits he'd brought. "Here, these are for you, from my grandmother."

"Thank you, Matteo, and tell your grandmother thank you."

The tutor and pupil opened their books and began to review the lesson. But Matteo was barely able to concentrate as he thought about losing his beloved teacher.

That night Matteo wept in his bed. He couldn't stay at home with his younger siblings—they were too little and bored him. He poured out his misery to his grandmother Laria when she came to say goodnight. She went to Giovanni and insisted that he hire new tutors to continue Matteo's studies. He did so, but it was soon obvious that none was as engaging as Father Bencivegni had been.

Matteo was the first of many children born to Giovanna Angiolelli and Giovanni Batista Ricci. A prominent citizen of

Macerata, Giovanni naturally assumed his first son, Matteo, would follow in his career path. Giovanni was not only descended from a noble family, but also had worked hard and was a prosperous businessman. His sights were set high for his son and he hoped he would go far beyond their little hilltop town.

Then in 1561, Giovanni learned from a business associate that some Jesuits were arriving in Macerata to open a school where boys could attend free of charge for a complete education in the humanities taught in a highly disciplined manner. He immediately knew that Matteo would want to attend, but he did have doubts.

Giovanni disliked religion intensely, yet he was keenly aware that these new Jesuits were becoming known for providing the highest quality education possible. That night he talked about it with his wife.

"I just don't want Matteo to start wishing to be a Jesuit himself," he said.

"Giovanni, they offer the best education, and it's free. We know Matteo has a mind for academics, so we must encourage that strength."

"The risk is that he will lose his interest in business," said Giovanni, shaking his head. "He's already more attracted to the little stories from the Bible that your mother tells him than he is in what I have to say about running a pharmacy! But all the best families in Macerata are sending their sons to this new school. Sending Matteo would assure his status. He might find a place in the papal administration."

His wife nodded in agreement.

The next day, on his way to his shop, Giovanni enrolled his son in the new Jesuit school.

⌇

Matteo didn't know which made him happier—the challenging lessons he now received every day from the Jesuit teachers or being around the other bright boys like himself who, in good cheer, competed with each other academically. Every day in his new school felt like a fantastic adventure, and soon Matteo's shyness gave way to easy friendships with the other students.

The rigorous academics intimidated him at first—the teachers demanded he pay attention and absorb lots of information. But Matteo was intrigued by how his teachers made their subjects fascinating and fun. Six days of the week, the boys were immersed in Latin and Greek studies. Matteo memorized Roman poetry and studied Greek prose. He wrote compositions, completed lengthy translations, and took classes in rhetoric. The Jesuit teachers created competitions and gave prizes to those of outstanding achievement. In addition, mornings began with Mass and prayers, and students were encouraged to go to confession at least once a month.

It didn't take long for teachers to notice Matteo's unusual focus, his ability to retain complex ideas and facts and remember long passages of text. As Matteo grew into his teen years, these abilities gave him confidence, and he was more and more drawn to the Jesuit way of life that combined virtue, spirituality, and knowledge. Most interesting to Matteo was that his Jesuit teachers seemed invigorated by a purpose, a higher calling than the ability to earn money or reach an impressive position in society.

His father's worst fear was coming true.

Chapter Three

ROAD TO ROME

To the relief of his parents, Matteo agreed to enroll in law school in 1568 at the age of sixteen. Secretly, the boy was certain that legal matters would never interest him, but it was important to secure his future—at least that is what his father said.

After many tearful goodbyes to his siblings, his beloved grandmother Laria, and his parents, Matteo left home and traveled by carriage to Rome and to La Sapienza University. As Giovanni Battista watched his oldest son disappear into the landscape, he sighed sadly. But he was sure this was good for Matteo—the university was known for educating sons of the ruling class and Matteo's choice of studying jurisprudence would certainly lead to an even finer profession than that of a pharmacist. That night he told his wife of his deep wish that Matteo would earn himself a noble title. The boy had demonstrated such a quick intelligence that this was a real possibility.

A noble title could not have been further from Matteo's

mind. Rome! It was the capital of the Papal States and of Italy. It was the beating heart of the Catholic world. Matteo's own heart now beat with excitement as he approached the densely populated city. At the gate, a guard inspected all his belongings, making sure that no heretical Protestant writings would cross into Rome.

Inside the walls, the city was a labyrinth of streets and plazas filled with men and women from Spain, France, and Germany, as well as Florentines, Milanese, Corsicans, and other Italians. Matteo stared in awe as he passed palaces and gardens, yet even within the city walls he noticed rough open spaces, like the countryside he'd just left.

Once he settled in the university, he couldn't wait to get out and explore the streets. He found the Pantheon, the Theater of Marcellus, the Capitoline, and numerous monuments still under construction.

He found the Vatican. What a thrill to know that Pope Pius V dwelled within its walls, a pope who worked with great determination to stem the Protestantism that was sweeping through Europe. Matteo had heard this pope's spirituality was fierce. Did he really wear a hair shirt underneath his habit and walk about with no shoes, as rumor had it? He imposed severe punishment for adultery and blasphemy, Matteo had heard, and had forbidden horse racing. This pope was so frugal that he dismissed the papal court jester and eschewed all luxuries.

Matteo mulled all this over as he went for walks, exploring Rome's streets and neighborhoods. The smell of delicious food he never knew existed wafted out to the street from restaurants and cafés on every corner. He marveled at the golden sunlight playing across the elegant architecture at different angles morning, afternoon, and evening—and he flushed with embarrassment when young women, obviously prostitutes, called to him from their doorways when he passed.

He was lonely. After he closed his books at the end of the day, he wished he could tell his grandmother about what he'd learned and all that he'd seen. She would always listen to him with great attention and share her own memories and lessons she'd learned from life. Ah, to be in the warmth of the kitchen, with the fragrance of his grandmother's pheasant stew filling the air.

"Matteo!"

The next day on his way to class he heard his name shouted out from the crowd of students, and scanned the scene to see who was calling him. It was a schoolmate from Macerata, Girolamo Costa!

"You're here too!" exclaimed Girolamo, who pushed his way over to Matteo. The boy was shorter than Matteo, with dark curly hair and a broad smile. "I was just wondering how I might get in touch with you, my friend. What class are you in?"

"Girolamo—yes! I'm here at university, in the law school," said Matteo as other students hurriedly brushed past him. "The classes are not interesting so far, but perhaps they'll get better. It's good to see you, friend! I've been missing my friends."

"Listen, I am late for my class, but I've just joined the Sodality of the Annunciation at the Roman College of the Jesuits," said Girolamo. "Another Macerata boy is there—Giulio Alaleoni, remember him? Why don't you join me this evening? You'll like it there—the conversations are fascinating."

Matteo readily agreed and the two friends made arrangements to meet that evening. As he rushed to his class, Matteo's heart soared. He was no longer alone!

He slid into his chair moments before his professor began the lecture on the history of civil codes. As Matteo focused on the professor's words, he recalled the readings he'd done the night before. He'd taught himself a strategy for memorizing the driest material as a way to keep interested—to see each code as a room, with each part related to an object in the room. His lips moved as he silently recited the codes, and then smiled when he realized he'd gotten them all right.

That night he was Girolamo's guest at the Jesuit Roman College as the sodality, or fraternity, gathered. These young men met informally to discuss the teachings of Ignatius, but sometimes they simply talked about their beliefs and hopes for their futures within the Jesuit society.

Matteo said little, but watched and listened intently to the lively conversations around him. Every person seemed to burst with ideas and opinions—they talked about Horace, Ovid, and Virgil; about Aristotle, Epictetus, and Seneca. They talked about traveling to Japan and even China as missionaries, and starting schools for children who would otherwise have no education at all.

One handsome, dark-haired young man from one of the wealthiest families in the region stood up and declared he'd turned his back on a large fortune to become a Jesuit, for which he had no regrets.

"But I don't intend to spend my days in a life of cloistered silence," he said with a laugh, "but to fight infidels and heretics, and spread the Catholic faith far and wide!"

"Do you wish to be a martyr, then?" called out one of the others.

"Perhaps, if it comes to that," the handsome young man replied with bravado.

Matteo, listening intently, doubted that his faith would lead him to martyrdom. Or would it?

"To quote Francis Xavier," said a strong-muscled young man from across the room, "'To the greater glory of God!'"

The group erupted in cheers and began to disperse for the evening.

Matteo returned to these Jesuit meetings with Girolamo as often as he could. Each night he left with much to reflect upon. No one was surprised when Matteo announced that he wanted join the Jesuits and take up the missionary challenge to change the world.

"I am willing to serve Christ wherever I am sent!" Matteo blurted out to Alessandro Valignano, the master of novices at the Society of Jesus.

Alessandro smiled at this young man, apparently a law student who'd had a change of heart, who had knocked so vigorously on the Roman College door just moments before.

Alessandro was respected—sometimes even feared—by the students. Rumor had it he'd lived a wild life years back. Like Matteo, he also started out studying law at the insistence of his father, a wealthy, influential man. But the story that was whispered among students was that when Alessandro was a teenager, he'd gotten into trouble and was accused of slashing a woman's face with a knife. For this crime, he spent more than a year in a cold, damp Venetian prison. In that long year, in the midst of suffering from lack of food and little human contact, he realized all he had lost because of his impulsive behavior.

Once out of prison, Alessandro was determined to show his family that he'd changed, and enrolled in Padua University to study law. There in 1566, he had a strange experience—one that he told only a few friends.

He had been preparing to go to bed in his tiny room at the university after an ordinary day of classes and studying. Kneeling down before a small wooden icon of Jesus that he brought from his home in Chieti, he closed his eyes and began to pray. Suddenly, he felt a gentle warmth wash over his body. At the same time, he heard the words *You are here to help others experience the love and forgiveness of God.* Clear as the text in one of his schoolbooks, the words seemed etched in his mind. Looking around the room, he noticed the light of the flickering candle on his desk and wondered what had happened.

The next day, he requested admission to the Society of Jesus and was immediately accepted.

Because of his skill at organization, Alessandro was appointed supervisor of the novices. And though he was physically tall and imposing, personally he exuded a kindness and charm that put students at ease.

He now listened intently to Matteo Ricci and observed a fervor and intelligence, which were precisely the characteristics Jesuits looked for. Alessandro had invited the young man to come into his office and now sat opposite him. He had a good instinct about him and proceeded to pose many questions— about Matteo's family, schooling, and, most important, the origins of his desire to become a Jesuit missionary.

"I feel as if . . . I was born to be part of the Society of Jesus," Matteo blurted out. "My first tutor, Niccolò Bencivegni, gave me my first lessons in mathematics and astronomy, as well as the beginning of Latin and Greek. He showed me the world through knowledge, the world that God has made. And this knowledge has given me, well, a joy that surpasses all other joys. I want to bring this . . . this awakening . . . to as many other people as I can."

"And are you now prepared to renounce the world and relinquish all of your possessions?" asked Alessandro, studying Matteo's response carefully. Young men naturally were filled with ambitions and desires of all kinds.

"I renounce the world and all its temporal goods," Matteo said, his eyes bright with intensity. "I promise to do whatever my superiors believe is most useful, and to go wherever they wish me to go, for the glory of God."

"I see your sincerity in commitment and willingness," said Alessandro, nodding with approval. "Please arrive at the house of Sant'Andrea at the Quirinale tomorrow morning, where all novitiates give up their earthly items. You will, of course, also need to sit for entrance examinations."

The next morning, Matteo arrived as he had been instructed, carrying a small pack of his clothes and books. These were all gently taken from him by one of the fathers, and in return Matteo was given a clerical habit, a coat, four shirts, a book of Latin grammar, a book by the African-born Roman poet Florus, and *Mirabilia*, the ancient guide to Rome.

As soon as he was settled into his room, Matteo sat at the desk and wrote to his father, telling him the news.

Giovanni was deeply upset. He crumpled the letter from Matteo in his hand and stalked out of the house and into the small grove of orange trees behind it.

No, he would not send a return letter, he decided. *I will*

go to Rome myself to tell him in person that this is not acceptable. Giovanni turned to go back into the house when he saw that his aging mother had followed him. She had been in the kitchen and was still wearing her apron.

"I found the letter you tossed to the ground," said Laria softly. "And I beg you to think of Matteo as the young man he really is, not the boy you wish he would be. Allow him to have his own life. Don't be angry with him."

"Nonsense, of course I think of him as he is—he has a great mind and can accomplish much in this world, as long as he doesn't veer off into a life of irrational thoughts and unrealistic dreams," Giovanni huffed.

"My grandson Matteo knows himself and has chosen a spiritual path," Laria countered. "No one can make him change his mind, of that I am certain."

Giovanni raised his hand to say he did not wish to discuss the matter further with his mother, and brushed past her to find his servants and ask them to prepare a carriage to go to Rome the next day.

The following morning, finally en route after a fitful night of sleep, Giovanni was set with determination. The air was clear and warm, the sun already creating shadows behind the olive trees they passed.

Giovanni reviewed his indignation as he looked out at the scene. First his mother and then his wife had tried to dissuade him from going, but he knew he could make Matteo change his mind. The road was full of holes and stones, which made the carriage jerk uncomfortably. As the sun rose in the sky, the air became hot and dry, and Giovanni began to feel ill. After several hours, his face was flushed, and as he glanced at the passing fields, he started to lose focus and feel confused.

When the carriage driver stopped at the town of Tolentino, Giovanni nearly fell to the ground when he stepped out. The other passengers carried him into a nearby store and to a cot the storekeeper kept in the rear supply room.

They fanned him and put a cool cloth to his head, but Giovanni was overtaken by a fever, and he remained on the cot for several days. In spite of the good care the storekeeper and his wife provided, Giovanni tossed and turned, until finally the fever broke on the third day.

From the cot, he looked around at the small wooden room, at the shelves with empty jars and the bundles of straw stacked on the floor. What had happened to him? Giovanni's mind slowly focused on his predicament. Perhaps this trip was not to be. And maybe this was for good reason. After all, his son Matteo was nineteen—a man! He could choose his own destiny. *Who am I to try to determine my son's future? He will find his own way.*

As soon as he could, Giovanni Battista rose and thanked the kind storekeeper, gave him some money for his troubles, and sought a carriage that could take him back to Macerata.

Chapter Four

A MISSIONARY SPIRIT

Girolamo Costa and Matteo Ricci, sweat dripping from their faces, were on their hands and knees scrubbing the floor of the kitchen.

Each was thinking the same thing: *Is this drudgery really required to become a Jesuit?* They wanted to voice their frustration about the backbreaking work, but they had already begun their required year of silence.

Outside, warm spring sunlight filtered through the trees that lined the streets, and vendors called out the goods they sold from carts. But inside the kitchen of Sant'Andrea at the Quirinale, the air was humid and still. For Matteo and Girolamo, the city life—the bustle of markets, the chatter of happy families on outings, the good cheer of young friends greeting each other—was far, far away.

As soon as they were finished cleaning the floor of the kitchen at the novitiate, where all the new candidates received their training, the two young men rinsed their rags and, without speaking, left to change their clothes and go to the chapel. A breeze wafted through the windows, but they didn't even glance out into the street. The first year with the Jesuits, their daily routine of cleaning and prayer was done in silence, and they received no lessons from teachers.

This customary start of the training, designed to instill humility in students, became difficult for Matteo. At first, he threw himself into the menial tasks, happy to be living a life of sacrifice. But as months went on, he longed for intellectual stimulation and missed talking about mathematics, Greek, philosophy, and the other subjects with his fellow students. Learning, for Matteo, was nourishment, as critical to him as food.

He thought about his grandmother as he drifted off to sleep one night, and wished he could tell her all about his new life in Rome. *What is she doing now?* He thought of his parents too, but they never understood him, so their images slipped away from his mind easily. But his gentle grandmother, with her warm smile and sense of humor . . . how he missed the comfort of her presence.

In his mind, he talked to her. *I find a comfort in the silence we are forced to keep here. It reminds me of when you used to tell me stories when I was little as we sat before the fire, and when the story ended, we would just look at the fire in silence together. Do you think this is the presence of God?*

While in prayer for hours at a time, Matteo relaxed in a deeper sense than ever before. And when he was cleaning the rooms, disposing of trash, or sweeping the hallways, he began to feel that presence in those times too.

God, it seemed to him now, was never far away.

He also thought about Alessandro Valignano. Matteo had heard that his superior was recently appointed Visitor to the Indies—he was now director of all missions in the Far East. *What a great honor!* thought Matteo. *He is doing the very work that Jesuits are called to do.* He also wondered, *Is he lonely being so far from Rome or is every day a new adventure?*

One morning, as he left the kitchen to toss out a bucket full of dirty water, a young woman about his age walked by, holding the hand of a young child. The woman's golden hair caught the sunlight just as Matteo caught sight of her. His stare was so forceful that she turned and smiled at him.

"*Buongiorno,*" she said with a slight nod.

Matteo smiled back at her, then blushed and looked down. She walked away, making a little joke with the child, and Matteo returned to the kitchen. *Some women are so beautiful*, he thought. When he was younger he imagined he would have a wife and children one day. But now his desire to be a Jesuit was so strong that he no longer considered a woman in his future at all. He enjoyed observing happy families and couples interact, but he considered his new calling as something much bigger and more important than living in common society.

The following spring, Matteo, now twenty-one years old, took the vows of poverty, chastity, and obedience. He agreed to have little or no contact with his family back in Macerata. From this day on, his Jesuit brothers were to be his true family. He swallowed hard at this and felt a tug in his heart, but this was his new path, and he must agree.

Matteo was admitted to the Roman College on September 17, 1572, at the height of the Renaissance, a period in which learning was held in the highest regard. It was also the year that the Jesuits celebrated the fact that Ugo Boncompagni, a strong supporter of the Society of Jesus, became Pope Gregory XIII. This meant papal support for all of their missions.

His year of silence finally over, Matteo was eager to begin his studies. He excitedly introduced himself to his new roommate— Giulio Fuligatti, a student who loved mathematics as much as he did.

"Did you see the schedule of classes?" Matteo asked Giulio.

"Yes, daunting, for certain," replied Giulio. "Ignatius himself designed the entire academic program. Two years of rhetoric and three years of philosophy—"

"And three years of theology," Matteo added. "I can't wait to hear the famous theologian Roberto Bellarmino lecture on Thomas Aquinas."

"And I look forward to studying Aristotelian logic and metaphysics," said Giulio. "I think we'll be reading the stoics Epictetus and Seneca in the ethics classes. Truly, Matteo, we may have renounced our worldly goods, but these studies are a richness beyond comparison."

"Indeed, Giulio," Matteo agreed.

But the professor who quickly captured Matteo's attention was Christopher Clavius, a German astronomer and mathematician who'd been ordained in 1564. He was the most prominent Jesuit mathematician of the times, famous for having written an annotated translation of Euclid's *Elements of Geometry*—the book that was a teaching guide to fundamental mathematical theory and processes, including geometry and number theory. When he was just twenty-three, Clavius had observed a stunning total solar eclipse that caused him to decide to study astronomy for the rest of his life.

Matteo was riveted when Clavius told the class that some

astronomers were beginning to doubt the belief that the earth was the center of the galaxy—a belief firmly held by the Catholic Church. Instead, they argued that the *sun* was the center of the universe. Clavius disagreed with this new idea, but he told his students that he listened to these astronomers with respect—no true scientist should rule out seemingly absurd ideas. What Matteo didn't know was that Clavius heard the arguments from a young mathematician and astronomer from Pisa named Galileo. The sun was the center of the universe, insisted Galileo, but he could not convince the older man.

Clavius believed that spheres orbited the earth, including the sun, moon, Mercury, Venus, Mars, Jupiter, and Saturn. Stars existed beyond the planets and further out was God's dwelling. Like all Jesuits, Clavius considered science and theology to be intimately interwoven—to understand mathematical principles and laws of the cosmos was to know the greatness of God.

In the evenings, Matteo and Giulio often studied together and discussed their revered teachers and all they were learning.

"I'm starting to think that cartography is the most challenging subject," Matteo said, half to himself and half to his listening roommate Giulio one night.

"Challenging to *you*? You seem to grasp the concepts of all subjects quite easily," Giulio replied.

"I mean challenging to the way men think of the world. We only know a little. Cartography helps establish what men know now so that explorers can use it to then expand that knowledge, just as Cristoforo Colombo has done, and other navigators."

"Very true. Who is the teacher?"

"He's Flemish—the cartographer Gerhard Kremer," said Matteo. "He recently completed the first map with lines of latitude and longitude, which help ocean navigators plot courses more accurately. And Kremer constructs globes and sundials, all of which he will teach us within the next months."

"So you will always know where you are and where you are going," Giulio declared with a laugh.

"Exactly!" said Matteo, laughing with his friend. "And he has an astrolabe, just as my first tutor did. Now I see how important it is for sea captains to determine the distance from the horizon to particular stars or planets. Along with a map and a compass, it's an invaluable instrument for determining one's location."

"So we can never be truly lost, is that what you mean?" asked Giulio playfully.

"With God's help, no," replied Matteo.

Matteo's imagination came alive whenever he studied a map. The jagged country borders, the vast areas of ocean, the unfamiliar names—it all intrigued him. *What do those vast unpopulated lands look like? What plants and trees grow along these winding rivers? How do those northern mountains appear in brilliant summer sun?* He had ventured far from his home in Macerata to come to Rome, and now his desire to travel had grown—he longed to see the worlds that lay beyond the Roman College.

Under Gerhard Kremer's guidance, he'd learned how mapmaking had evolved and become more and more precise. He also learned how to make a globe and was so proud of his achievement that he placed it on a table in the middle of the room he shared with Giulio. Whenever their friends came to visit, they could not help but comment on this curiosity.

"All right, Matteo, show us where we are on this globe—

surely I must be at the top!" joked Girolamo, peering at the round object.

"I'm not going to tell you—you must learn to use the globe, and it's obvious where Rome is located," replied Matteo as Girolamo and the others gathered around.

"Matteo, what are all these coils and pieces of metal?" interrupted Giulio, who stood next to his roommate's desk, on top of which was a neat pile of tiny bits of metal.

"Pieces of a mechanical clock," said Matteo. "I'm teaching myself to make one."

"Is there nothing this brother can't do?" said Oliviero Toscanelli, who'd recently made a formal request to become a missionary and now sprawled across the only comfortable chair in the room. "If you can make a mechanical clock that rings on every hour, then you can make anything."

"I haven't done it yet, Oliviero, so you save your praise," said Matteo.

"Show us how you can memorize whole pages at a time!" Oliviero would not give up. "Here, take this page of this book," he said, picking up *Geography* by Ptolemy, choosing a page about cartography, and handing it to Matteo. "I've heard that you can memorize a page of text after reading it through just once."

The others in the room urged Matteo to show them what he could do.

"All right," said Matteo, taking the book in his hands and slowly reading the page. After a few minutes he handed the book back, closed his eyes, then began to recite it from memory as his friends tracked the words on the page. Though he hesitated a few times, Matteo spoke confidently, and when he reached the end, the men erupted in whoops of amazement and joy.

They clapped Matteo's back, congratulating him, then finally began leaving to return to their own rooms.

As Oliviero reached the door, Matteo asked him quietly, "Do you know if you are to be accepted as a missionary?"

"No, I've heard nothing yet," said Oliviero, becoming serious. "Alessandro Valignano is very particular about such assignments. It will happen eventually—it must. I have had many dreams of traveling far from here to foreign countries to save souls."

Matteo considered his friend's words and realized he shared that same feeling. He longed to travel to the farthest reaches of the world to save souls. As his friends drifted from the room, Matteo knew it was time to put in his own formal request to be sent out as a missionary, wherever he may be needed. The world was full of men and women who unknowingly suffered from a lack of knowledge of God and the saving grace of Jesus Christ. It was his duty as a Jesuit to save them.

Once he made this decision, Matteo's desire to be a missionary grew more urgent day by day. Soon, nothing else really mattered.

Chapter Five

LEAVING ITALY

The image often came to him at night as he drifted into sleep: a crowd of thousands of men and women in India, looking up in unison, their hands clasped together in prayer, and a shining cross hovering above them.

The conversion of the entire population of India to Christianity—outlandish, impossible, yes, but he could not shake this idea. It taunted him, as if daring him to make it come true.

Matteo was not the only one with this vision—many young Jesuits at the Roman College spoke of such a widespread transformation and how it could be accomplished. Jesuit missionaries, they believed, had the power to convert people all over the world. Matteo was fixated on it.

But he was forced to wait.

Before he left for Japan, Alessandro Valignano designed a selection process for determining which students should be chosen for missionary work. The superior general, Everard Mercurian, an older man with large dark brown eyes, considered a young man's physical stamina for the long ocean voyage and harsh conditions of living in foreign countries. He also evaluated emotional strength—could a young man endure months or years of loneliness, homesickness, and frustration in communicating with people entrenched in their own religions and primitive customs?

Matteo knew that he met the criteria, but he wasn't sure that the superior general was convinced.

Some students at the Roman College who applied for missionary work came from prominent noble families who could exert influence on behalf of their sons' wishes. Matteo's family had no clout in this regard, and Matteo watched as one after another son of a wealthy father was sent off overseas to a glorious adventure.

He put in his request again and again over a period of two years. Each time he was rejected he refrained from bitterness, and instead turned to his studies, taking on more complicated lessons. In the evenings he retreated to the corner of his room where he was teaching himself how to make a chiming clock.

At last, at the end of 1576, Martino da Silva, the Procurator of Missions for Portugal in India, came back to the Roman College for the purpose of gathering a new group of missionaries— and Matteo was chosen and assigned to the Indian province of Goa. Now, at age twenty-four, Matteo would be heading to this prosperous port city that was annexed by Portugal from the sultan of Bijapur, an Indian kingdom. Sitting on the western coast of India on the Arabian Sea, Goa felt as far away as the moon—Matteo's heart leaped in joy at the prospect of the adventure of his life.

The group was divided into two; Matteo was placed in the first group to set out on the journey. With him were Francesco

Pasio from Bologna, Italy, and Rutger Berwoutz from Belgium. The men were given two weeks to prepare for departure. Matteo felt a pang of sadness—was there time to see his family?

The superior general was a kind man who understood better than the younger men what they were about to undertake. Fixing his warm dark eyes on them, he suggested that they quickly travel to their hometowns to bid goodbye to their families. Then he spoke to Matteo in particular.

"My son, I know you have not seen your family since coming to the Roman College five years ago," he said. "I urge you now to go to them, spend time with them, especially your grandmother, who I know you are close to. This mission may be many years."

Matteo lowered his eyes before the superior general. He thought of the long journey to Macerata, of greeting his mother, father, grandmother, and siblings. And then, in the same breath, say goodbye?

That night he tossed and turned in bed. His heart was divided—he longed to see his family, yet the powerful emotions that arose at this thought pulled his heart away from his missionary purpose. Finally, as dawn broke and the soft morning light filled his small room, Matteo realized he would not see his family. He was a missionary—and that meant poverty and sacrifice. He would not go to Macerata.

It was possible that he would *never* see his family again, and that he would never set foot on the campus of his beloved Roman College, which had so deeply influenced and formed his sensibilities. These thoughts made him sick and he tried to push them aside. He could not let them hold him back from his larger purpose.

He turned his mind to the fact that the pope had asked to see his little group of new missionaries before they departed.

This was magnificent! Pope Gregory XIII believed that the future of Christianity was in the hands of Jesuits like these young men who bravely set out to bring the teachings of Jesus to people who would otherwise live in ignorance. His approval meant everything to them. Matteo deeply revered Pope Gregory—after all, he had recently commissioned Christopher Clavius to create an astronomically accurate calendar.

At the appointed hour of this important audience with the pope, Matteo bowed deeply, as did the other young missionaries. As he rose, Matteo studied the old pope's face and thought that his long white beard and piercing blue eyes made him look like God himself.

The old man gazed back down at the young men from his high-backed wooden chair. He blessed them and prayed for their safety.

Chapter Six

THE DANGEROUS JOURNEY

A little boy pushing his cart full of melons along the dusty street on the way to the market turned a corner and stopped short. A group of wide-eyed young men with odd-shaped bundles and bags were standing in front of the elegant façade of the Roman College, talking in loud, excited voices. *Who are they?* The boy decided to rest a minute and watch them.

"We will change the world!" one shouted, and the others laughed.

It was a beautiful May morning in Rome, 1577, and the air was cool and birds darted between the treetops. The men stood together in front of the Jesuit school, waiting as horses were readied to begin a long journey.

Matteo checked his bags for the tenth time. He had packed little clothing, but he was bringing his astrolabe, a quadrant, one of his mechanical clocks, and several pieces of crystal glass. Whenever he held these up to the light, he marveled at the metaphor of God's light shining through a person's soul, creating beautiful colors that were so pleasing.

He'd folded these carefully into his clothes, along with a square piece of wood upon which the Virgin Mary and Jesus were painted. He'd purchased it from a priest who was an artist in Rome and who painted icons like this to give away freely, his own form of evangelism.

Matteo and the others hoisted bags onto their backs and began their slow journey, heading first to Genoa along Via Flaminia. From there they kept on traveling to Spain. Some of them, like Matteo, had never been outside of Rome and they thrilled at the new landscapes and towns. Everywhere they went, people stared and wondered about them. They ate and slept little—they were full of missionary fervor, and each step brought them closer to their final destination. When they were hungry or hot or suffered blisters, they remembered the suffering of Jesus and made no complaint. To be a missionary was to suffer.

In the evenings when they made campfires, they spoke about their dreams for converting towns, cities, even whole countries! They were set to arrive in Lisbon in July.

It was a brilliant, hot summer day when they caught sight of the red-tiled rooftops and cobblestone streets of Lisbon that crisscrossed the gently sloping hills. The sea sparkled in the distance. Once in the city, they stared at the throngs of strange-looking people from far-off countries crowding the streets. Their stares were returned—these Jesuit men, in their dark clothing, stood out as obvious foreigners too.

The streets were alive with noise and activity. Just nine years earlier, the great plague had killed many citizens. Sebastian, king of Portugal, built two hospitals in Lisbon for the sufferers and had called for doctors to come in from Spain to help. He arranged for the care of widows and orphans, and granted scholarships to students of the University of Coimbra.

The missionaries found an inn with small but comfortable rooms. They soon learned that monsoon season was imminent, which meant their sea journey could not begin for another nine months. They were disappointed and unsure what to do.

Matteo had long before figured out that the best cure for boredom or impatience was to dive into his studies. He enrolled in the University of Coimbra to learn Portuguese and study philosophy. A few months later, the second group of Jesuit recruits arrived from the Roman College to join them: Rodolfo Acquaviva, Nicholas Spinola, and Michele Ruggieri.

At last, in the following March, 1578, the date of their sea journey was set. The new general of the Jesuit order, Claudio Acquaviva—Rodolfo's father—had already sent his blessing from Rome.

King Sebastian, who was the same age as the young missionaries, insisted that they visit him before departing so that he too could give his blessing. The young king was an enthusiastic would-be adventurer. He got a vicarious thrill as Matteo described their journey ahead to India. An ardent Jesuit, Sebastian dreamed of his own military glory. He wanted to fight Muslims in Africa, though he was not physically strong, as he'd been sickly his entire life.

Years later, Matteo was to learn that Sebastian had indeed died in battle.

At last, the fourteen Jesuits—including the Procurator of Missions for Portugal in India, Martino da Silva—boarded three large Portuguese ships. Matteo was assigned to sail on the *São Luis*. He stood on the dock and watched with fascination as the crew loaded salted meat, wine, oil, rice, water, and biscuits into the cargo hold. The Portuguese had been seafarers for generations; their crews were skilled and their vessels were sturdy. Among the passengers boarding with Matteo were merchants of spices and silks, soldiers, and men who sought adventure in foreign lands. The Jesuits were traveling free, but they were expected to serve as chaplains for the crew, passengers, and the handful of African slaves.

The ships eased out of the harbor and finally coursed through cool, deep waters. The Jesuits' excitement abated as the ship heaved and rolled, and they took turns vomiting over the railing. As soon as he could stand without feeling ill, Matteo sought out the captain of the *São Luis*. He was eager to see how he used the maps and navigation instruments. Captain Paul Maolo was a man of few words who preferred to have no contact with his passengers. But he quickly saw that Matteo's interest was not idle, and allowed the Jesuit into his quarters to examine the maps.

"This carrack appears to have working cannons—do you expect we might need them?" asked Matteo.

"*São Luis* was a war vessel," replied the captain, whose browned, wrinkled face seemed set in a constant scowl. "But pirates roam the coastal waters, ready to take advantage of an unprepared crew. The cannons will be used if we need them."

"How many months will we be at sea?" asked Matteo, shifting uncomfortably. He'd never imagined pirates overtaking this ship, but of course that was common.

"No voyage can be accurately predicted—wind shifts and storms cause delays. If all goes well, we will reach India in six months," said the captain, who then eyed Matteo. "As a man with an understanding of navigation, you will be interested to know that we will follow nearly the exact route taken in 1498 by

Vasco da Gama, the great Portuguese explorer," he said, his dark eyes flashing.

Matteo realized the tremendous pride the captain felt by association with the explorer.

"I'm honored to sail with you," said Matteo. "May our journey be safe and without trouble." He bowed his head, thanked the captain for his time, and went to join his Jesuit friends.

As days went by, the passengers enjoyed watching the sunrises and sunsets, and fished for sharks, which were plentiful in the water. One morning an unidentified ship appeared in the distance and the crew became uneasy. It followed the *São Luis* for half the day and Matteo feared it was pirates. Would it attack? By evening, the mysterious ship slipped away, but now everyone on board was watchful for a surprise return.

At night, Matteo studied the positions of the constellations he recognized. He was among the young astronomers who believed the earth was round, which made the flat horizon almost more interesting to observe. Matteo found a friend in Michele Ruggieri from Puglia, who had entered the novitiate just a year before him. Lively, talkative, and always ready to laugh, Michele had also left law studies to join the Jesuits, and enjoyed discussing theology with Matteo. As Easter approached, the two Jesuits were determined to hold Mass on the ship. They heard confession from passengers and crew, and Matteo observed how Michele's friendly, outgoing nature put everyone at ease.

But as the weeks wore on, existence on the ships became difficult. They crossed the equator and headed toward Brazil to catch a strong westerly wind that could push them southeast in the direction of the Cape of Good Hope at the tip of Africa. The heat at times was suffocating, supplies of food and water were getting low, and since no one could wash their clothes or their bodies, the human stink grew pungent. In addition, some passengers became ill with scurvy from lack of eating fresh fruit.

Matteo admired the captain's skillful navigation through the strong currents around the Cape of Good Hope. Inwardly he was relieved. He respected and feared the sea, in part because he could not swim. His fear intensified the next day, when the sky was dark in the morning and got even darker as the day went on. Soon a violent storm enveloped the *São Luis* with gigantic waves, tossing the heavy boat around like a toy. The Jesuits huddled with the terrified passengers, and Michele—who was usually the most positive of one of the group—threw reliquaries into the sea. Passengers went onto their knees and loudly confessed sins. Every time a pounding wave hit the ship, Matteo thought they would perish. Surely no vessel could withstand this violence for long.

But the storm abated at last and the waters calmed—most felt it was a miracle that they had survived. Matteo gathered passengers to pray their thanks.

More storms awaited them—as did a vision.

Two days later, as all three ships sailed north through the wide Mozambique Channel on the southeastern coast of Africa, the sky darkened, rain began to spatter over the deck, and within hours the waves rose to great white peaks. Lightning shot down through the low gray clouds, followed by deafening claps of thunder. The passengers screamed and scurried below deck, but some, including Matteo and Michele, remained above. They preferred to cling to the rigging than to be pressed into the suffocatingly small cabins. Suddenly a tremendous wave crashed over the bow of the ship, sweeping one of the crewmembers over the side. Matteo watched in horror as the man slid helplessly over the rail and slipped from sight into the turbulent water.

Then—fire! Long jets of fire seemed to shoot out from the ship's highest masts. Matteo tried to make sense of what was happening. A sailor shouted "Saint Elmo's fire—the Sacred Body!" Screaming in terror at the fiery light that neither rain nor waves extinguished, the men on deck ran for cover.

Matteo scanned the deck searching anxiously for Michele, then spied him—he stood with his face upturned, streaked with rain. He was shouting as if addressing the Blessed Virgin—he seemed to see her hovering atop the mizzenmast. Soaking wet and gripped with fear, Matteo watched in astonishment as Michele smiled at the lashing fire while the ship rocked violently. Matteo went below and joined the frightened passengers, and soon after, Michele appeared. He announced with a strange calm that the boat would be safe.

"It is quite normal for the Blessed Virgin to protect sailors in rough seas," he said.

Matteo had not seen the vision, but he had no doubt that Michele did, and admired him for it.

By dawn, the waters had flattened. But the passengers were still badly shaken. They sat with their heads in their hands or praying quietly. Some retreated to their hard, narrow bunks and turned their faces to the wall. Matteo understood—he too had believed they would die.

The captain came to check on everyone.

"What do you say, Captain—was that fire last night indeed the Blessed Virgin?" called out one of the men. "After all, the storm did die down after that."

"I don't know about the Blessed Virgin," Captain Maolo said gruffly, "but there's no harm to the ship from this event. We call it Saint Elmo's fire. We've seen it before, many times, in storms just like that one."

The captain had a bigger concern: The third ship, the *Bom Jesus*, was nowhere to be seen and he feared it had perished. As tension mounted, Matteo and Michele visited with each of the passengers, sitting and speaking to them in soothing tones. When a fight erupted between two men over a tiny bit of bread, they pulled them apart and tried to console them.

The *São Luis* and *São Gregorio* headed for the Mozambique harbor, where in late July they dropped anchor. Dominican brothers from nearby residences came to greet the Jesuits, inviting them off the boat for much-needed food and a place to rest for several days.

With food and peaceful sleep, Matteo's energy was quickly restored, and he reflected on the terrible storm and his friend's vision of the Blessed Virgin. All of it had shaken him to the core. He was certain they had survived so that they could do their work as missionaries.

He was glad when the ship was ready to complete the journey a week later, but his enthusiasm vanished when he saw several hundred African shackled slaves being marched onto the ship to be placed in the lowest cargo hold. Matteo's stomach tightened. He'd already seen passengers suffer who had more space than these slaves did—how could the slaves possibly survive? The two ships set sail, and soon passed over the equator and journeyed up into the Indian Ocean.

The heat became thick; moans and wails could be heard coming from the cargo hold where the slaves were confined. Matteo and Michele confronted Captain Maolo—was he going to just let these men die? Could he not allow them to come above deck at least some of the day for air and water?

Captain Maolo shook his head no without even looking at them. Distraught, Matteo, Michele, and the other Jesuits went to the slaves and sat near them, giving them water and trying to give comfort, knowing their words were not understood.

One by one, the slaves began to fall ill and die. At first their dead bodies remained in the cramped space, but after the Jesuits vociferously complained, the captain ordered their bodies thrown overboard. Matteo was in anguish. These were human beings, children of God—they deserved dignity, not to mention air, food, and water. Yet this was the captain's ship, and Matteo was helpless to free the slaves unless he considered mutiny.

Seven weeks later, on September 13, 1578, the ships arrived in Goa, a coastal region of India. Miraculously, the third ship, the *Bom Jesus*, had arrived just a few days earlier. The ship's crew referred to Goa as Little Lisbon, for thousands of Portuguese citizens lived there. The Portuguese military leader, Afonso de Albuquerque, had swept through the region in 1510, killing all native citizens in his path and seizing control from the sultan of Bijapur. The reign of terror that followed included the destruction of hundreds of Hindu temples by Portuguese soldiers. But Albuquerque was not interested in moving further into the country. Since Goa was an ideal stopping point for trading ships, he wanted only to control the coastal region.

Passengers and crew stumbled off the boat, and the surviving slaves were led off in chains. Matteo, Michele, and the other Jesuits, now sunburned and gaunt, slowly made their way to the landing. The six-month journey had aged them. They had suffered from extreme hunger and thirst. They'd been forced into close quarters with strangers. They had helplessly watched healthy human beings deteriorate and die, and nearly lost their own lives, and faith, in the violent storms.

They were eager to set foot on this land, which to these young men was sacred. Francis Xavier, the first Jesuit missionary, had founded the Jesuit College of Saint Paul forty years before, and his remains were actually here, in the church. He had longed to enter China, but was denied.

Matteo's deepest wish was to finally fulfill Francis Xavier's dream.

Chapter Seven

INDIA

The Jesuit men threw their tired bodies and belongings down on a patch of grass.

"It is very, very good to be on solid ground," said Michele.

The others nodded. A light drizzle of rain fell and the air was humid and fragrant. It was a new country, a new continent—India!

Though exhausted, the friends, who had traveled on different boats on the long journey, were delighted to be together again. Their sense of humor was immediately restored as they sprawled on the grass, imagining what they would all do in this foreign land. Could any experience be more difficult than the last six months at sea? Michele, at thirty-five, was about ten years older than the others, and he jokingly announced that they would now all head off to China. In fact, he declared, he would assign them to their new duties: Matteo would teach mathematics, Rodolfo Acquaviva would teach theology, and Francesco Pasio would offer lessons in philosophy.

"And I, Michele Ruggieri, will offer legal counsel, as necessary," he ended with comic flourish.

"What castles of air you've created in your mind!" said Matteo, laughing. He admired Michele for his outgoing nature.

"Don't laugh—all this could be so," said Rodolfo.

As they continued their banter, Matteo stared out at the harbor. The calm gray water stretched far into the horizon. The journey had scarred his spirit. He felt stronger for having survived, but he realized that he would probably never set off for another journey with the same naïve optimism that he once had. Anything could happen.

The men eventually rose and gathered their belongings and began to walk away from the sandy coast on their way to the city of Goa.

The Jesuit recruits walked through the streets of Goa looking for the College of Saint Paul. Even though the whole region was ruled by a viceroy and a council of Portuguese businessmen, throngs of Arabs, Venetians, Persians, and Turks mixed with the many Indian and Portuguese citizens who filled the markets. Matteo stopped for a moment when he saw African slaves, some of whom he recognized from the *São Luis*, standing on a platform so that buyers could examine them. His heart sank and he felt unable to move. What would happen to them? Rodolfo had to pull him away from the scene to keep up with the others.

Encountering so many unfamiliar races of people, the Jesuits could not help but stare. Matteo caught Rodolfo staring at a young woman with dark skin, almond-shaped eyes, and delicate gold earrings who returned his look with interest. Now it was Matteo's turn to pull Rodolfo away.

Finally arriving at the doorstep of the Jesuit College of Saint Paul, the travelers were relieved to be warmly welcomed by the Portuguese brothers. The hosts immediately offered the new arrivals a large meal of delicious foods made with spices the men had never before tasted.

The next day, Matteo was assigned to teach Latin and Greek to students at the attached mission school—an almost effortless task that left him plenty of time to renew his own theological studies. He was greatly relieved to be back in a Jesuit community with its daily rituals, and a school where learning was the primary activity.

But the humid tropical climate sapped him of strength, and he often retreated to the coolness of his room. Now, as he sat at his desk near a window looking out onto a courtyard, he listened as young students played a game of handball, and marveled that the heat that weakened him had no effect on the boys' energy.

Whack! The youngest boy hit the ball surprisingly hard, causing the others to burst into laughter.

The weather wasn't the only difficulty in Goa. Matteo was learning that the Portuguese methods for converting Hindus or Muslims were brutal, quite unlike what he'd been taught in the Roman College. So-called heretics—Hindus, Muslims, and Jews—were harassed and humiliated. Matteo was dumbfounded to hear that some were actually burned at the stake with no protest from the Jesuits.

Hindu and Muslim people who did agree to convert to Christianity had to give up their cultural traditions, trade their given names for Portuguese names, and dress like Europeans. And any native citizen who wished to work in the homes of the Portuguese had to first convert to Christianity. *What kind of conversion do they hope to obtain this way?* Matteo thought. *Surely if it is contingent upon employment, conversion will only be superficial and short-term.*

Whack! The ball ricocheted far back into the courtyard and the schoolboys shouted in glee.

Exasperating Matteo further was a rule that men of India who pursued the priesthood were prevented from studying philosophy or theology. The reason for this, he'd learned, was that these Indians should not become too proud. Or did the Portuguese just want to maintain their superior position?

Whack! Two boys argued over whose turn it was to run after the ball this time.

Matteo's anger rose at the injustice of the situation. *Why shouldn't Indian priests receive a complete education—they would be better priests for it, wouldn't they? Denying them this education could very well cause resentment that could lead them to abandon their faith,* he thought.

His arguments were not well received by Portuguese priests who at first looked at him as though he were a naïve visitor, then became angry when he would not give up. Finally he dropped the subject. What could he do? *I will write to the superior general in Rome explaining why these rules actually work against true conversions,* he decided.

All missionaries were expected to write to the superior general regularly to keep Rome informed about their experiences as missionaries in far-flung parts of the world. They might not like hearing Matteo's views either, but it was a risk he was willing to take.

He knew for a fact that Alessandro Valignano would never approve of these tactics—he'd always stressed that missionaries should respect the cultures of the people they wished to convert. The way to do this, Alessandro had suggested, was to learn everything about a foreign culture—even adapt to it to a degree—and develop trust in people who wished to convert to Christianity.

Trust and kindness, he said, were essential.

The school bell rang out and the boys ended their game. Matteo watched them run in the blazing heat back to their classrooms.

The stagnant situation—no one knew when they would continue on to China—and the relentless, stifling heat were slowly wearing down Matteo's spirit. From his room, he had a view of pineapple trees and whitewashed buildings dappled with sun. He could also see several cashew trees with their bright red fruit. A pretty scene indeed, and yet he felt dead to it and was filled with melancholy.

He closed his eyes and imagined the animated faces of his friends and teachers in Rome. *I remember them, but do they remember me?*

As months went by and he still received no foreign assignment, Matteo became moody, withdrawn, and impatient with his students. *Will I be teaching Latin to children forever?*

One morning as he rushed to class, he stumbled and fell, hitting his head. Two Jesuit teachers found him unconscious on the ground in the baking sun, and they quickly brought him inside and called for help. A fever took over Matteo as he lay in bed, and he was too ill to eat for many days.

The Jesuit priests were worried. They valued Matteo as one of the finest teachers in their school, and insisted that he take time to regain his strength. They also wanted him to be happy and sensed that he needed a break from the intense teaching schedule. In November of 1570, they sent Matteo to the coastal city of Cochin, four hundred miles south of Goa, to recuperate in the small Jesuit community there.

In Cochin, the weather was balmy and pleasant, and Matteo had time to study and reflect. He turned inward, spending many hours in prayer, in addition to a few hours of teaching—which he did only because he was told to do so. He found no joy in it; his heart was in theology studies, which he found endlessly fascinating and satisfying.

Seasons came and went, and near the end of one year, his superiors in Cochin surprised him. They deemed that he was ready to be ordained as a priest.

In a ceremony with only a few witnesses, the bishop of Cochin placed a plain white stole over Matteo's shoulders and anointed his palms with holy oil. Matteo Ricci became Father Ricci on July 26, 1580. "On the feast of Saint Ann I sang a solemn Mass to the great rejoicing of the fathers and my pupils," he wrote to his former professor at the Roman College.

Finally well and feeling strong, he made the return journey to Goa. Upon arriving, he learned that his friend Rodolfo Acquaviva had left to become the superior of a Jesuit embassy at the request of Mohammedan Mughal Akbar, a great Indian ruler.

Michele Ruggieri had been sent to Macao, a Portuguese enclave in southeastern China—where Alessandro Valignano had spent many months—to prepare to enter into interior cities of China. He wrote to Matteo, complaining how hard it was to learn the complex classic Chinese language, and added that converting Chinese to Christianity would be hopeless unless he could learn.

He also requested that Alessandro arrange for Matteo to join him in Macao; he badly needed his friend's help. Alessandro saw the wisdom of allowing Michele and Matteo to work together. These two bright young men could support—and comple-ment—each other in establishing a Jesuit presence in Macao.

In April 1582, Matteo received the assignment to sail to Macao, with a note that he should depart as soon as possible.

At last! Matteo's only disappointment was that he was leav-ing Goa in exactly the same state as when he arrived three years earlier. The Portuguese were still using cruel conversion meth-ods, with predictably poor results. His suggestions for how it could be done differently were ignored.

All I've really accomplished here has been to teach lots of stu-dents the rudiments of Greek and Latin. I could have done that anywhere. He tried to put this bitterness aside and pack.

Michele had written him with a specific request: to bring a mechanical clock—two, if possible. Michele had discovered that the Chinese were fascinated by them. Items such as the clock, Christian icons, and even common crystals could draw them in to discussions about science, and that often led them naturally to spiritual matters.

Francesco Pasio boarded the ship with Matteo, as he'd been assigned to go to Japan. The three-month voyage encountered no significant dangers from India to China, but midway through, several passengers fell ill with a severe fever. One morning, word spread on the ship that two people had died in the night. The following day, Matteo felt his skin grow hot and realized that he too had the deadly fever. He retreated to his bunk and Francesco ministered to him day and night, placing cool cloths on his fore-head and trying to give him water.

As days went by, Matteo grew weaker and could barely raise his head. In the midst of a feverish delirium, his body began jerking and his arms flailed. Francesco tried to shake his friend awake, but Matteo pulled away from him. "I'm flying," he moaned, "over the ocean . . . ."

In his hallucination, Matteo had left his sick, sweating body to soar over the sea on warm currents of air. In the dream-vision, an albatross appeared flying next to him, a white bird against the sharp blue of the sky. It was powerful, with a wingspan of eleven feet, and he could feel the draft caused by its heavy flapping wings. The albatross glanced at Matteo with one eye, then took the lead. Matteo followed the bird up to a mountain that hung in the sky. As they both landed softly on the rocky mountainside, Matteo realized that he had trusted the bird to show him the way—he had no human power left to know what to expect or where to go.

"What is your name?" he asked the bird.

"Xavier," the albatross replied.

Yes, Matteo would let the albatross show him the way . . . .

He awoke with Francesco shaking his shoulder and peering at him with worry. Sensing he'd been on the brink of death, Matteo now knew that he very much wanted to recover.

"It's all right now," he said to Francesco. His skin was cool and his dark hair was matted against his head.

Francesco slumped back in his chair, relieved at last that his friend appeared to be getting better.

Matteo silently reflected on his vision. He knew well that Francis Xavier, the most famous Jesuit missionary, began as a fun-loving student at College of Saint Barbara years before. The story went that at first Xavier wanted nothing to do with his roommate, Ignatius of Loyola, whom he guessed did not approve of his loose lifestyle. *Yes, venereal disease is running rampant, but the fun is worth that risk, isn't it?* Xavier reasoned to himself, feeling invincible as young men often do.

But Ignatius, keenly sensitive to the nuances of human character, won over Xavier by quoting just one sentence from the Bible: "For what is a man profited if he shall gain the whole world and lose his own soul?" That stopped Xavier. He dropped his judgment and began to listen to his roommate's talk about spiritual practices, about helping the poor, about changing the world.

It was Xavier, some years later, who became the first Jesuit missionary to India and Japan, enduring constant hardship.

Now Matteo gripped Francesco's arm and rose from his hard wooden bunk. He stood and walked unsteadily up the steps to the deck. The air was clear and cool; the sun shone brightly. He held onto the railing and took a deep breath.

When the ship finally reached the city of Macao, with its high stone walls, Matteo walked stiffly down the gangplank carrying his heavy bag. He was paler, thinner, and quieter than when he'd left India. But now, at twenty-eight years old, he was intent on reaching his good friend Michele Ruggieri and together venturing into the wild lands of China.

Chapter Eight

ENTERING CHINA

Macao was an isolated Portuguese province located on a peninsula in southeastern China. Vasco de Gama had first visited the area in 1497, and the Portuguese established it as a trading post in 1557. For this right, they paid the Chinese an annual fee.

When Matteo arrived in Macao in August 1582, the population was about 10,000 people. He eagerly scanned the crowds, fascinated by the small stature and long dark hair of the Chinese. Portuguese citizens were everywhere too, and because Macao was a thriving trade city, its crowded streets included Africans, Indonesians, Malaysians, and Indians; many foreign men had married Chinese women, so children of mixed backgrounds could be seen as well.

Most seemed poor, but Matteo spotted some officials dressed in fine silk who carried parasols for protection against the brilliant sun. He'd learned from a fellow ship passenger that Macao had distinct wet and dry seasons, and that in the summer, typhoons tore through the area. Matteo was grateful that his ship had not encountered such a storm.

Now he and Francesco Pasio trudged up the winding streets, away from the heart of the city to a less-populated outlying series of streets, in search of the Jesuit residence. At last they spotted it and their hearts leaped with joy. Michele Ruggieri shouted happily when he opened his door to find Matteo and Francesco at his front step, weary but smiling. He immediately brought the travelers into the cottage and offered them food. Francesco wept in gratitude.

"I want to hear about your voyage, but first I must tell you that Father Valignano was here just last month—on his way back from Japan," said Michele, making sure his friends settled in comfortable chairs, then darting around the small fireplace where he had a pot of fish stew warming over a small flame.

Matteo waited expectantly. All three men regarded Alessandro, their former novice master at the Roman College, with tremendous respect. He was thoughtful, wise, and compassionate, but also a man of action—he'd built churches and schools and organized whole dioceses. He represented exactly the kind of missionary they each wanted to be.

Alessandro's approach was unconventional. "If we missionaries are to have any lasting effect," he often told his students, "we must understand and respect the customs of the people." This was quite the opposite view from those who believed in intimidating or even killing anyone who was not Christian.

"He created guidelines for missionaries while he was here—and they are so intelligent, so logical," said Michele. "Father Valignano says Christianity must be presented as welcoming and accessible, not as a harsh religion that punishes people for following different paths. That, he says, goes against the Gospel teachings, and it incites fear and rebellion—creating the very opposite of what we want."

Matteo nodded in agreement. It had been easy to fantasize about converting millions of Chinese while he was in Rome, but once he was face-to-face with people who were deeply attached to their ancient traditions, Matteo realized how foolish his assumptions had been.

"We are not trusted here because we are Italian," Michele continued his rush of conversation—he was so happy to finally talk to old friends. "As you've probably already observed, the Chinese are very proud of their culture and confident of its superiority. They suspect foreigners of plotting an overthrow, or of trying to establish control over the population. Therefore it is of utmost importance that we keep our true purpose here a secret. We are not permitted to venture outside of these walls—I have tried to journey to other regions, but was always stopped and sent back. Valignano says that the Chinese people would be receptive to Christianity if they were given the chance to really understand it."

"And that's what we're here to do," said Matteo with a smile.

"Yes. But this can only happen if we're fluent in Mandarin, the spoken language of educated people, as well as all the local dialects of the poor. Languages were never easy for me—not Latin or Greek, but Mandarin is simply mind-boggling," said Michele, sighing with frustration. "At least I've finally understood the hierarchy of officials. I'll explain it to you simply. The emperor of China is named Wan-li, also called the Son of Heaven. He lives in Beijing, in a massive fortress called the Forbidden City—no one is allowed in unless expressly invited by the emperor. Each province has its own officials who are able to govern somewhat independently."

Michele brightened as he remembered a bit of good news. "I have had one success, however. A man who works here as an interpreter—he speaks Portuguese, Italian, and Mandarin—he was curious about us and has actually converted to our faith. He's been extremely helpful, working as an interpreter and also explaining the hierarchy of government officials. Still, I can't depend only on him—I want to learn Mandarin, and hope you and I can learn together."

"Of course," replied Matteo. "But even before we've mastered the language, we need to immerse ourselves in the culture. I want to understand what makes people happy here, what they long for, what they believe in."

Michele passed a bowl of fish stew to Matteo and Francesco, and the three friends ate and talked well into the evening.

Matteo unpacked his astrolabe, mechanical clocks, crystals, and other items he'd brought all the way from Rome, and put them on display on the cottage porch where passersby could see. They quickly caught the attention of neighbors who stopped to look and ask questions. With the interpreter's help, Matteo gave simple lessons in astronomy and geography.

He saved afternoons for walking the streets, sometimes for hours, discreetly taking note of the religious garb worn by Macao citizens. Clearly quite a few people were Buddhists, but many were Taoists and followers of Confucius. He was mystified to learn that some people apparently followed all three religions, if you could even call them religions. But what were their central beliefs? Did they have one god or many—or none at all? And were social castes associated with these belief systems?

At Matteo's insistence, he, Francesco, and Michele began eating only dishes that local people ate—rice, fish, and vegetables—and they did their best to master the use of chopsticks.

"Learning a language that looks like a jumble of paint strokes? It's a waste of time," said the Portuguese fisherman to his friend.

The two old men were walking by the grounds of the Jesuit residence on a hillside dotted with bauhinia trees with bright pink blossoms and mango trees with fat green leaves. Through the window of a cottage, Matteo and Michele could be seen testing each other with Mandarin phrases, Michele throwing his hands up in despair each time Matteo corrected him.

"The Chinese will never allow real interaction between their people and Europeans—especially not those Italian priests," said the fisherman. "So why bother to learn such a difficult language when it will never be put to use?"

The old friends shook their heads in agreement.

No foreigners were allowed to cross the high walls of the Portuguese enclave without official permission. Chinese soldiers holding sharp spears patrolled the walls of Macao with vigilance, on guard for pirates or would-be conquerors who might try to trespass in disguise. Neither did they care for Christian priests who tried to persuade Chinese people to abandon their traditional religions—Buddhism or Confucianism.

It didn't take long for Matteo to feel that the Portuguese-dominated Macao was like a prison, and he was eager to travel. Michele remarked on the importance of sending gifts to officials—it often helped to soothe their fears about foreigners, and was part of a delicate social system of showing humility and respect. When he'd sent a pair of reading glasses to one provincial governor months earlier, Michele was surprised how welcoming that official suddenly became, hinting that he would allow the Jesuits to travel throughout the province. But political shifts could be quick and decisive, and unexpectedly that official was ousted from his government position. Michele's gifts had been sent in vain.

In the Macao Jesuit residence, Matteo withdrew into prayer in the small chapel; there was so much to absorb and try to understand that he needed time in quiet contemplation. It was pouring rain outside, which made the gray sea blend into the gray countryside. Inside, the chapel was damp and chilly, and as he knelt to pray, his desire to travel felt so strong it was almost painful. Just days before, a letter from Alessandro Valignano arrived for Francesco, directing him to join Alessandro in Japan—he was needed there as soon as possible. Matteo and Michele sent their friend off with good wishes, but could barely hide their envy.

Alessandro's words came back to Matteo again and again: Friendship had to accompany evangelism. Getting to know people—understanding their circumstances, their desires, their life struggles—and offering compassion would instill trust. And that would lead to the love of God, the teachings of the Gospel.

But they had to meet Chinese people in order to even begin, and this was much more difficult than Matteo ever imagined. The Chinese he observed on the streets of Macao were poor and seemed burdened by just trying to survive. He could only guess at their beliefs or morals.

He had no answers. Language was the way in, he knew this. He asked God for the courage to keep studying Mandarin, no matter how strange and difficult.

While Matteo and Michele discussed this dilemma, their young Chinese interpreter, who had taken the Italian name Filippo, listened and took note. Filippo had been born in Macao, where he'd converted to Catholicism and the Jesuits had been extraordinarily kind to him. Now he was somewhat of an outcast among the Chinese, and the Jesuits provided him with a place to live and a small salary in return for his work as interpreter. Without telling Matteo or Michele, Filippo contacted an administrative official named Wang Pan and told him of Matteo's skills as a mathematician and astronomer.

An educated man who read and wrote poetry, Wang Pan was intrigued and sent an official invitation, asking Matteo and Michele to visit him in Zhaoqing, a region to the northwest of Macao.

The two Jesuits were ecstatic. Finally, the opportunity they had longed for—an official invitation to go outside the walls of Macao. Immediately they began to prepare for the trip, plotting how to blend in so as to avoid attracting attention. After Filippo told them that Wang Pan was a Buddhist, they decided to shave their heads and beards and don the gray robes of Buddhist monks.

"The hour has arrived," wrote Matteo to his friends in Rome, "when divine mercy turns his eyes to this miserable realm, and opens with a mighty hand the door shut tight to the preachers of the Holy Gospels."

The journey ahead was critically important—this could be the beginning of their foothold in China. They brought Filippo with them, of course, as well as several servants and many gifts—small crystals, a mechanical clock, and books.

It was a cloudy morning when they boarded a junk—a compact, efficient boat with fully battened sails. It eased through the busy Macao harbor, navigating around other junks carrying animals, people, bags of food, and furniture—and boats decorated with colorful banners that carried high-ranking officials.

The priests thrilled at the sight of the walled city of Macao receding in the distance as their junk angled toward the mouth of the Pearl River. Before long, they saw terraced hillsides and spotted farmers working in rice paddies. They passed many fishing boats and children scampering along the riverbanks. The junk made stops at several villages where Matteo and Michele marveled at the seemingly tranquil life of the poor inhabitants amid lush and fertile lands.

"The emperor—how far away is he from here?" Matteo asked Michele as they both stood at the railing, staring at the passing green countryside.

"More than one thousand miles," answered Michele, who then paused for a moment. "I didn't want to tell you the whole story when you first arrived, but I will tell you now. Wan-li began as an effective ruler with the guidance of an older secretary who cared for him since he was an infant."

"Yes, you told me about him," said Matteo.

"But I did not tell you . . ." replied Michele, faltering. "When that secretary died, Wan-li was freed from every moral and official restriction. Since then, he has abandoned his governmental duties and keeps himself hidden in the Forbidden City with his many concubines, guarded by thousands of eunuchs. They say he takes opium, which is why he's reclusive."

Matteo looked at Michele with shock as he continued. "Wan-li is served and protected by the eunuchs—these men are domineering and violent. And like most Chinese, Wan-li trusts no foreigners."

After a moment, Michele said at last, "So, you see, Matteo, this is actually a very dangerous place for us, and the closer we get to Beijing, the more dangerous it will be."

The country's ruler taking opium and dominated by an army of eunuchs? It sounded unbelievable and frightening. Matteo instinctively turned to face the north, as if he could visualize Wan-li, far away, seated on a golden throne deep in his palace.

One day, one day . . . I will go there, he mused. *Frances Xavier would try if he were alive today. Because he'd know that if a missionary could influence the emperor of this vast country—even one so dangerous and unpredictable as this one—then a conversion of thousands or even millions of people might be possible.*

The sun broke through the clouds and threw its sparkling light on the muddy water of the Pearl River as the junk cut a smooth path north.

Chapter Nine

TROUBLE IN ZHAOQING

The woman seated on the elaborately carved wooden chair was beautiful. She had the whitest skin and darkest hair Matteo and Michele had ever seen.

The priests and Filippo had been invited into her presence by her husband, Wang Pan, and were now transfixed by her twinkling eyes and small mouth, the corners upturned into a slight smile. She wore a dark blue robe, and her smooth black hair was twisted in a knot atop her head. Her small white hands rested on the arms of the chair, and Matteo could not help but stare at her disturbingly long fingernails—like talons they curled down several inches from her fingertips.

Her dark eyes darted over the two men, then looked down shyly. Matteo looked down too, and noticed her tiny misshapen feet enclosed in purple silk embroidered slippers. He recalled with a jolt that the feet of girls of many well-off families were bound tightly soon after birth, and continued to be all their lives. *How can she walk?* He winced at the thought.

After being introduced to Wang Pan's wife, Matteo and Michele were unsure what to do, then quickly remembered to bow deeply. When he rose, Matteo noticed sadness in the woman's eyes. He pulled from his pocket a small cloth bag and handed it to Wang Pan, indicating that it was a gift for his wife. Her eyes widened as she took the bag and opened it. She pulled out a small piece of Venetian glass.

To the surprise of everyone, Wang Pan snatched the crystal and handed it back to Matteo. "I am sorry, we cannot accept your gift," he said.

Filippo whispered to Matteo and Michele. "He cannot take the gift because it will be perceived by others that you are buying his influence—and if he is seen as supporting foreigners, he would be ousted immediately."

Matteo glanced up at Wang Pan's wife and saw that her smile had vanished.

Ushering the Jesuits into his official room of business, Wang Pan began asking questions of Matteo about science and mathematics. He was obviously an educated man and extremely curious about the Jesuits. Matteo answered all of his questions happily—what a marvel to encounter a man who had curiosity about science! Many Chinese were superstitious and regularly made critical decisions based on perceived omens and signs. But Wang Pan was more rational than that, or so Matteo thought.

"What we wish, honorable sir," said Michele, "is to obtain a piece of land here in Zhaoqing, in this small, quiet town, as a place of retreat."

"We have traveled far," Matteo added, "coming from India, seeking to build a chapel."

The two Jesuits kept their words to a minimum, not wanting to overwhelm their host.

Wang Pan nodded. "I am willing to provide land here so that you can build your residence," he said, "but on one condition."

Matteo and Michele straightened.

"You must not invite any other Jesuits to join you," said Wang Pan, his face set. "The governor is afraid of an invasion of foreigners. I cannot afford to be seen as the man who invites trouble."

Matteo and Michele bowed deeply in thanks. Though they were quiet and kept their eyes low, inside they were euphoric.

The priests and Filippo returned to their temporary housing located on the edge of the Xi Jiang River, passing many shops and homes, all with curved rooftops that lifted up at the corners. Once inside their house, Matteo and Michele burst out in excited laughter.

"At last, we will establish a Jesuit residence!" shouted Michele.

"I didn't think he would say yes!" said Matteo. "Father Valignano will be so happy. Our work can really begin now."

"Did you notice? Wang Pan—he is genuinely curious about us," said Michele. "I think he is a potential convert!"

Filippo, who had been quiet up until then, finally spoke up. "I must inform you both—Wang Pan has another reason for inviting you here."

Matteo and Michele stopped and stared at him.

"It is well known that Wang Pan has long wanted very badly to have a son. Even after many years of marriage and relationships with several concubines, no son has been born. He hopes that by welcoming you as Jesuit priests, your God might grant him this wish to have a son."

Matteo slumped into a chair. "So I've misunderstood Wang Pan. Even though he is educated and interested in science, he is just as superstitious as the common people. How naïve I have been to hope he would be different."

"Ah, but think of Wang Pan's wife," said Michele. "You could see the depth of her sorrow at not being able to have a son."

"A woman who cannot give birth to a son can be cast out of marriage forever," said Filippo quietly.

"Remember the biblical story of Abraham and Sarah—they believed that Sarah could not bear a child because of her age. And yet, she did!" Michele was always the most cheerful of the three. "God does not give out favors to wealthy, powerful, or superstitious men. Still, miracles do happen."

"So then, our success as missionaries—does it depend on Wang Pan's wife having a son?" Matteo asked.

The Jesuits' newly constructed home in Zhaoqing was a one-story compound designed in a western style, with a central hall that looked out upon the Xi Jiang River. Matteo's room on the second floor faced the river, and he enjoyed spending hours there in contemplation or watching the many merchant boats—water travel was the fastest mode of transportation for the delivery of food and other items.

To the north, the Jesuits had a view of the massive mountain peaks called Qixing Yan, often shrouded in mist. Nearby stood the Chongxi Pagota, a prominent octagonal-shaped tower constructed with brick and stone that was built to ward off disaster, particularly flooding.

One morning, Matteo was startled to see a junk the size of a small house easing up the river. It seemed to have many bedrooms, and Matteo could even see a hall with a long table for banquets. He heard the voices of children playing within the boat and caught sight of several women peeking out of the windows. Surely this was one of the "floating palaces" he'd heard about—boats owned by high-ranking officials.

He was interrupted by Michele, who was ready to continue their work on a Portuguese-Chinese dictionary. They had begun in Macao, and now with help from Filippo and others, it was finally taking shape. The priests worked on it diligently every day, knowing it would be a valuable tool for them now—and for all missionaries who followed in their footsteps.

In the afternoons, Matteo walked through the streets of the busy town. He wanted to get to know the marketplaces and he wanted people to get used to seeing him. He was intrigued to observe that shopkeepers used the abacus—a simple wooden frame with beads strung on parallel lines of wire—for their business calculations. He also noticed the degrading living conditions of the poorest people; dog waste floated in puddles where children played. And many people had a sickly, malnourished look. Matteo worried that if he or Michele were to become sick, they would have to travel back to Macao for medical help.

Some scenes were so disturbing that Matteo could barely absorb their meaning.

One evening, he invited Filippo to join him and Michele for a dinner of fish and rice. After a prayer of thanksgiving for the food before them, Matteo thought about how to pose a question.

"Please, you must explain the ways of the people to us," he finally said to Filippo. "Is it true what I have heard that men are able to purchase women to be their wives?"

"Yes, Father, this is what is done. A man may purchase a wife."

"And if he wishes to marry but has no money?" asked Matteo.

"He can sell himself to a wealthy family, to be their servant, and the family will marry him to one of their female servants."

The two Jesuits were quiet as they considered this. It seemed barbaric.

"Filippo, today I saw a man trying to sell a very little boy on the street," said Matteo. "I feel certain the boy was his son. I could do nothing, but it was a terrible sight. The boy was crying, but the father simply called out to anyone that he was for sale as a servant—at least, that is what it looked like to me, from what I could understand."

"Yes, Father, this is common among the very poor. And because girls cannot be sold easily, they are often killed just after birth." Filippo looked embarrassed to say this out loud, but he wanted the Jesuits to understand the extent of the poverty. He looked down, now very uncomfortable.

Matteo also wanted to ask about the many prostitutes he'd seen, but he suspected Filippo would have been overwhelmed with shame just at the mention of it.

"May God have mercy on them," said Matteo.

The three men cleared their dishes, and lit candles as the evening darkness filled the rooms of their new home.

That night, after he had prayed and was getting ready for bed, Matteo thought again about the father selling his son on the street, and of the prostitutes—young women and men—in the doorways of a desperately poor district. How could he, as a missionary, ever reach them? He could not solve their lifelong poverty.

A story came to mind of Ignatius of Loyola—the beloved

founder of the Society of Jesus. He wanted to fight the evils of prostitution in Rome, but his success in making converts was really due to the fact that venereal disease was running rampant among men and women of every social class. It wasn't too difficult to convince prostitutes to give up their immoral habits for a Christian way of life when the alternative was disease and possibly death—which they could see all around them.

Matteo didn't have that kind of leverage here in China. He couldn't even talk to people. Everywhere he went, men, women, and children gaped at him as if he were a monster. They'd never seen a tall European man with round eyes. It didn't matter that he wore Buddhist clothing, that he tried to be friendly and kind. He had to be far more cautious in his approach.

As he closed his eyes, Matteo felt the task before him was immense, impossible. He'd come all this way with such faith, but the obstacles were bigger than he'd ever dreamed. He prayed to Frances Xavier for courage to keep going in spite of the darkness creeping over his soul.

"Would that you could see me as I am now: I am a Chinaman," Matteo wrote to his friend Giulio Fuligatti. "In our clothing, in our looks, in our manners, and in everything external, we have made ourselves Chinese."

More specifically, Matteo and his companions dressed in the dark robes of Buddhists, which they thought would identify them as religious men, but more often confused the Chinese they encountered.

Now Matteo stood in the reception room of the Jesuit house, where he welcomed the group of local visitors whose attention was riveted by a small piece of Venetian glass. Matteo had placed the shining crystal on a pedestal for display just where the sun could shine on it, so that guests would notice it immediately.

The visitors marveled at the way the sun sparkled through the glass and created a rainbow of colored light on the wall. They were also fascinated by the astrolabe, the books, and a painting of the Virgin Mother and the baby Jesus that Matteo had brought all the way from Rome, and which now hung on the wall.

In less than a year, a son had been born to Wang Pan's wife, and news spread. Delighted, Wang Pan credited the Jesuits, and offered more protection for them. They needed it, as many local people were openly suspicious of the Jesuits and resentful that they'd been allowed to build such a large residence—in a foreign style—in such a choice spot by the river.

Matteo thought that by dressing as a Buddhist, he would ease their worries, but that was not the case. So he opened up the Jesuit residence for visitors to tour—and this was a success. Curiosity about the objects on display caused the visitors to drop their fears and ask questions, opening the way for long and winding discussions.

One day, Matteo observed a group of young mandarins— local men of the educated elite—bow deeply before the image of the Madonna and Jesus. Thinking it was odd, Matteo realized with a start that they might be mistaking the Virgin Mary for a female deity—possibly Guanyin, who was believed to influence the birth of sons. Were the visitors confusing the two? Matteo immediately wrote to the Jesuits in Macao asking them to send a painting of Jesus—if there was to be a face of Christianity, it should be that of Jesus!

But the object that captured everyone's attention was the map of the world. It had been made by Abraham Ortelius, a cartographer from the Netherlands, and was one of Matteo's most prized possessions. He stood next to it proudly, and showed visitors the directions of north, south, east, and west. He explained latitude and longitude, and pointed out the equator and the boundaries of China.

He also showed them the boundaries of Italy, Portugal, and India, hoping that by teaching people a bit of geography, they might not be so afraid of him. The visitors were curious, but the map made many of them uneasy and even angry. To them, the "Middle Kingdom"—China—dominated the world, and yet on this map Europe was at the center.

Seeing such reactions, Wang Pan suggested that Matteo create a new version of the world map, one with Chinese notations so that his people could appreciate its value without prejudice.

Matteo immediately recognized that this was necessary. He found a large table on which to work and began making sketches. For this map, he would put China at the center instead of Europe and add many notes of explanation in Mandarin for each country, mountain range, and body of water.

I will praise Wang Pan at the top of these notations, he decided. *It's good to keep our host and main supporter happy.*

While Matteo worked on the new map of the world, gossip flew about the Jesuits.

These strange foreigners, they know how to work magic.

They can turn plain metal into silver—I saw them do it.

They are just waiting for the chance to kidnap our children and take them to Macao to sell.

Matteo invited a clockmaker from India to visit so that he could construct a mechanical clock that the Jesuits could give as a gift to the governor. The clockmaker, a gentle soul with dark skin, set to work as soon as he arrived. But the appearance of the man—yet another stranger in the Jesuit residence—rattled their Chinese neighbors. The priests awoke at night as rocks landed on the roof and against the stone walls.

One evening, servants ran out of the Jesuit house and caught one of the boys who'd thrown rocks through their window. They held the boy briefly, scolding him for the damage he'd caused, then released him. When neighbors accused the Jesuits of unlawfully holding the boy captive, Wang Pan was forced to intervene to settle the commotion. He listened to the complaints of the people, and then came to the Jesuits and insisted that the Indian clockmaker return to Macao immediately.

Matteo was acutely aware of being watched by hostile neighbors wherever he went. When he walked through the village every morning, he kept his head down and voice low, but he knew his every move was tracked. At night, he slept lightly and awoke with a start at the slightest sound.

They were not welcome here. In fact, Matteo increasingly worried that tension was so high that he and the other Jesuits could easily be physically attacked, or even killed.

Chapter Ten

A LUCKY ESCAPE

Hostility was not the only reaction that the Jesuits inspired in Zhaoqing. Scholars, wealthy men, and educated officials were thrilled to meet the priests, and held elaborate banquets in their honor.

One such dinner was particularly full of lively, genial conversation. All through the many courses of food, the guests took turns asking Matteo and Michele questions about Italy: What did it look like? Who governs the people? How are disputes settled? What does the architecture look like? How far have their explorers traveled? Who is this person called the pope?

They wanted to talk about astronomy and mathematics and compare what Chinese scientists knew with the knowledge gained by the Jesuits. Matteo was keenly aware of the importance of etiquette and answered each question with care and respect. He wanted them to understand that he did not think of himself as superior to them, especially when he talked about the brilliant European scientists, like the astronomer Christopher Clavius.

After many hours, when the evening was winding down, one mandarin pulled Matteo aside to speak to him privately.

"You have profound knowledge, Father, and I greatly admire your understanding of the earth and sky. But . . . ." The mandarin hesitated, then faced Matteo and Michele directly. "You are living and dressing as impoverished Buddhists. It would be wise to abandon it. Dress and behave as the men of learning that you are, and you will discover more doors will open for you, and more people will to listen to you."

Walking home in the dark with Michele, Matteo could barely contain himself.

"Of course, he is right! If we ever hope to establish ourselves, we must associate with men of distinction, scholars—the literati," said Matteo. "Our dress must show that we are learned men, and therefore *they* will be open to our ideas. For now we are protected by Wang Pan, so we must keep our Buddhist dress. Perhaps if we take Chinese names, it will make us seem less like foreigners."

"I see the wisdom of that—as long as I can still call you Matteo!" laughed Michele. "Have you a new name in mind?"

"Li Madou," said Matteo. He'd been thinking of it for a long time, and it was good to finally say the name out loud.

Michele said the name several times, trying to perfect his pronunciation, then sighed. "I wish I could speak to people directly without having to rely on Filippo to translate."

Matteo bristled. He was increasingly frustrated with his friend's inability to learn the Chinese language. He was now fluent in Mandarin and could not fathom Michele's inability to retain what he learned.

And yet Michele's best qualities—his good humor and optimism—were a welcome antidote for Matteo's constant melancholy. He remembered how Michele had insisted on translating into Chinese—with Filippo's help—the Lord's Prayer, the Ten Commandments, the Hail Mary, and the Creed. These Mandarin translations now hung on long silk scrolls in the wall of the hallway where all visitors could stop and read them—they sparked many questions about the Jesuits' religion.

Although Michele struggled hopelessly with Mandarin pronunciation, writing was much easier for him. In 1584 he wrote a simple catechism book in Chinese—a basic text for understanding Christian beliefs. He titled it *A Veritable Record of the Lord of Heaven*, and in it he discounted fortune-telling, condemned polygamy, and promoted the sanctity of family. Michele also included concepts such as spiritual transformation, which he knew Buddhists in particular would understand.

As the two priests arrived back at their residence and went to their separate rooms, Matteo suggested to Michele to send the first copy of his book to Wang Pan as a gift. The official was still their only protector and supporter in this hostile land, and it was important that they stay in his good favor for as long as possible.

Michele's good nature sometimes brought trouble.

A young man who'd been recently converted often lingered at the Jesuit residence; he was attracted to the objects that were on display. One day, he begged Michele to borrow one of the Venetian crystals to show to his relatives. With some hesitation, Michele agreed.

Weeks went by, and after the young man did not return, Michele and Matteo began making inquiries. He'd apparently gone into hiding, but he sent word to a cousin, who then told his brother, who then told his aunt, who then told his uncle that he had seen Father Michele Ruggieri secretly meeting with a married woman in a house at the edge of town.

The story spread rapidly and crowds of angry people showed up at the Jesuit residence ready to take revenge. Once again, Wang Pan was forced to intervene. His policemen found the young man, who admitted that the accusation against the Jesuit was entirely false. "I just . . . I just wanted to keep the beautiful crystal," he said through tears.

Wang Pan announced that the young man's punishment was to be beaten in public. In horror, Matteo watched as three officials savagely hit the guilty man with heavy wood planks, and cried out for them to stop, but was ignored. Matteo and the other priests brought the severely wounded young man into their residence, where they cared for him. Nevertheless, he died the next day.

It wasn't the first time Matteo had witnessed extreme violence sanctioned by government officials. A magistrate could order anyone to be tortured or killed, even if the charges against that person were questionable or untrue.

This disturbed Matteo deeply, and he wrote of one incident to a friend in Rome: "The victims are beaten in public audience, on the back of the thighs, lying stretched out on the ground; they are beaten with a pole of the hardest wood, the thickness of a finger, four fingers wide, as long as one's two arms outstretched. The dispensers of the punishment hold the pole with both hands and use great force, giving now ten, now twenty, now thirty blows, showing great ruthlessness, such that with the first blow they often take away the skin, and with the other blows the flesh, piece by piece. From which many people die."

The result of this cruelty, Matteo observed, was that citizens lived in constant fear and anxiety, particularly when officials of any kind were in sight. They sometimes even feared each other, for false accusations could easily lead to punishment.

China often seemed an utterly impenetrable, alien world to Matteo, leaving him feeling defeated and hopeless. He'd fallen far short of his goals as a missionary, and wrote to his friends in Rome pouring out his distress. He asked them to pray for his missionary work, "since I find myself so tepid where it is necessary to go with great fervor, such that I have gained very little in these parts due to my unworthiness."

He found solace in sitting alone on the small balcony of his upper room, studying the mathematics and astronomy books he'd brought from Rome. Reading this fine writing and following the logic of calculations—nothing made him more deeply happy. He could almost hear the voices of his beloved old professors as he read them. These were precious moments, when he relaxed and gazed at the river with its many boats, and he gave up trying to make sense of everything he'd seen.

Buddhism intrigued him. Though some Buddhists, like Wang Pan, lived by the religion's principles, many Buddhist monks ignored their vows of chastity and had wives and numerous children—and many appeared to worship a network of lesser deities. Scholars and government officials called themselves Confucians, but that didn't mean they lived wholly moral lives. And Taoists tended to stay isolated, living on what they received from begging.

And what about the fortune-tellers? They were everywhere, and this indicated to Matteo that the people had the capacity for a strong faith, but it had unfortunately latched onto the occult.

He thought of Ignatius of Loyola and Francis Xavier. What advice would they give him? Missionary life was always painful, difficult, even impossible, Matteo knew that. The challenge here was find a path into the hearts of these people, so that he somehow demonstrate them God's love and forgiveness in a way they could understand.

The educated men—the scholars he'd met, and some of the wealthy landowners and officials—he had to start with them. Their curiosity about his knowledge of science was the door through which the teachings of Jesus might get in. And these men, in turn, would influence the poorer classes.

Alessandro Valignano had been tracking Matteo and Michele's progress from afar through their letters and reports from visitors who had seen them. In 1588, he decided that Michele—who still had not mastered the Chinese language even after his years there—would be of better use in Italy or Spain.

When he received this news, Michele solemnly began to pack his belongings. He could not hide his profound disappointment, but obedience was a principle the Jesuits lived by, so he would not utter a word of complaint. As Matteo watched his friend prepare for the long journey, he recalled the many years they'd known each other, beginning with the exciting times at the Roman College when they competed in debates.

"Our young selves in Rome would never have guessed the adventures we've had," Matteo said.

"Nor how difficult it would be to live and work here in China," Michele replied sadly as he wrapped a small silver crucifix in a piece of wood.

Matteo remembered the first convert they'd made within a week of arriving in Zhaoqing. He and Michele were walking along a rain-soaked road when they came upon an old man lying in the ditch under the leaves of a banana tree. He was covered with sores and too sick to get up. Michele had insisted they carry him to their residence, where they cared for the old man for several weeks, feeding him and praying for his recovery. When he regained consciousness, the old man was surprised and grateful that the foreigners had so lovingly cared for him, and asked to be baptized as a Christian. Soon after, he died.

"We must rejoice that his soul was saved, even if his body was not," said Matteo.

After that, the priests often crisscrossed the river to introduce themselves to merchants and passersby, and to offer simple lessons in Catholicism, even when they were met with blank stares. Still, they made twenty converts among the poorest citizens of Zhaoqing, and then to their delight, more followed. One man who converted to the Christian faith insisted his entire family convert with him. Each time Matteo and Michele were able to convert a man or woman, they celebrated with joy.

We were naïve, thought Matteo now, recalling how so many of their first converts quickly reverted back to their local superstitions.

"Michele, I hope you remember and feel proud of what we've accomplished in God's name here," said Matteo as he watched his friend sort out what to take with him and what to leave behind.

"I will, Brother," said Michele. "And I aim to tell everyone I can about it too. I hope to convince Father Valignano and others to send more funds for this mission."

"What I need, Michele, is to go to Beijing," said Matteo, who began to pace around the small room. "We need to meet Emperor Wan-li. That is my dream. If I can convince him to meet me and allow more Jesuits to come, then a true Christian foundation can begin. Otherwise, I'm afraid our work will come to nothing."

Michele turned to Matteo with a broad smile, "With God's help, and the pope's, it shall be done!"

The two men hugged before Michele departed for the boat that would take him to Macao. Matteo watched him go and silently prayed for his safety. His heart sank a little—he might never see this good friend again.

As if in sympathy, the sky turned gray and rain fell steadily for weeks after Michele left. From his window, Matteo watched with growing alarm as the river rose. He feared flooding was imminent. Although the Jesuit residence was built on a small hill, other nearby structures were not. The rain kept falling without letting up, and soon the muddy river water slipped over the banks and into the houses of their poor neighbors. The people of Zhaoqing panicked and ran from house to house looking for wood to reinforce their structures. Watching from the window, Matteo heard a crash below. He raced downstairs to see villagers smashing parts of the Jesuit house for the wood.

They stopped abruptly when he stood before them, as if ready to fight.

"Take what you need—quickly!" Matteo shouted.

They nodded at his words and continued to pull wood off the side of the residence. Matteo helped them gather it to carry to their homes.

After two more days, the rain finally stopped, and inch by inch, the water began to recede to the river. Matteo walked about the broken, muddy residence, examining the wreckage.

With the help of the servants, he made food to take to his neighbors, who grudgingly accepted his offers.

It was lonely without his friend Michele. As the weather returned to its usual heavy humidity and the servants worked to restore the damaged house, Matteo focused his attention on making small globes and mechanical clocks to give as gifts. He was now visited by educated men who wanted to hear what he had to say about geography and astronomy, and since it was proper to offer little gifts to visitors, Matteo made as many as he could to keep on hand.

At the end of a long, hot summer of living in virtual solitude, Matteo received a letter from Alessandro Valignano—he was sending a young Jesuit named Antonio de Almeida to work with Matteo in Zhaoqing, and described him as having "rare virtue and religious fervor."

Matteo knew of this young man, but was not prepared for his wildly zealous character. When Antonio arrived, he threw his arms around Matteo and declared that together they could convert all of China. Matteo showed him his room and was distressed to observe over the next few days that Antonio practiced severe mortification of the flesh, just as Ignatius had done. The young man ate nothing for days on end, flagellated himself with sharp tree branches until he bled, and wore a hair shirt day and night. It seemed extreme.

Matteo worried for Antonio's health—he needed the young missionary to be strong enough to travel with him to find people they could convert. What Matteo did not know was that they would both need strength for a hasty departure.

Wang Pan had taken a great personal risk by maintaining a

friendship with the Jesuits, and when he was promoted to another district, he reluctantly agreed to depart.

He was sorry to leave Zhaoqing, but officials had openly suggested to him that the Jesuits were foreign spies, and wondered why Wang Pan had allowed them to stay so long and mill about so freely. With great respect and sadness, Matteo and Wang Pan bowed to each other and praised each other in their final visit.

Matteo understood that the Jesuits were lucky to have enjoyed his support for so long. Clearly Wang Pan needed to protect himself and his family.

For some time after Wang Pan's departure, Matteo and Antonio lived in peace in Zhaoqing. Antonio's fervor alternately amused and disturbed Matteo, and the two made daily trips into the city and surrounding countryside, speaking to all who were interested about their Christian faith.

Their freedom ended abruptly when a new viceroy named Liu Jiezhai was appointed.

Tall and thin, Liu Jiezhai glared at Matteo and Antonio with hostility when they first paid a visit to respectfully introduce themselves. Liu Jiezhai disliked the sight of the two foreigners and had no wish to become friendly with them—that was obvious. He sat at his desk stiff and unsmiling as they spoke to him. After the priests left his office, Liu Jiezhai instructed his guards to watch their every move. In two weeks, he sent Matteo a letter by messenger, demanding that he and the Jesuits leave Zhaoqing immediately and go back to Macao.

Matteo was angry. He had committed no crime. In fact, he had worked very hard to establish good relationships with all the local mandarins. He forced no one to convert—he would never do that. Yet Liu Jiezhai was a cunning, corrupt official, he could see that clearly. In a letter to Alessandro, Matteo described the official as "a cruel, ambitious man, a friend of money." To confront Liu Jiezhai, Matteo would be walking a fine line between showing respect and showing strength.

Matteo chose a sunny, cloudless day to pay Liu Jiezhai a visit, and walked along the rocky road to his official residence. He bowed deeply before the official to show respect, but when he rose, Matteo proceeded to challenge the official's command for the Jesuits to depart.

"We have lived many years at the residence in peace," he said. "On what grounds must we leave?"

Liu Jiezhai bristled furiously. It was an affront that his authority was questioned.

"You must leave immediately. Go back to Macao—they don't mind foreigners there," said Liu. "If you are afraid to take that journey, I will give you money to hire guards."

"I will not take money from you." Matteo knew that this was a serious breach of etiquette, but he was ready to challenge the official's authority, at least in this matter. He looked right into Liu Jiezhai's eyes. "Again, I say, we have caused no trouble here. Allow us to relocate to another province and you will never see us again."

"Why should I allow that? You do not belong here or anywhere in China."

Matteo paused for a moment and then said, "We have made many friends among the wealthy men of this province. They know who we are. If we are forced to leave, they will soon learn that it was your order, and they will not think well of it."

Liu Jiezhai did not blink, but turned and spoke to his secretary next to him, then stood and left the room.

"You may move to another province," said the secretary, and then he too turned and left.

Matteo allowed himself to smile as he breathed a sigh of relief.

He and Antonio had little time to pack up their belongings and say goodbye to their newly converted Christian friends who would continue living at the residence. The priests took a moment to pray that the new converts would find the strength and courage to worship as Christians without the priests to guide them.

It was August 15, 1589, a heavy, humid day. Walking from room to room one last time, Father Matteo Ricci, now thirty-three years old, considered that he had been more sad than happy in this beautiful home at the river's edge. He turned and left through the front door, and wearily headed down the path toward the junk that would take them to a new home.

He had come to China to make converts, but it seemed all he was making were enemies.

Chapter Eleven

A LIVELY NEW FRIEND

The Jesuits traveled along the Xi Jiang River for many days, gazing with interest out at the passing landscape of rice paddies punctuated by stretches of oak forest. The air was so hot and thick with humidity that Matteo could not get comfortable. He was glad he could sit in silence for this slow river journey.

When the boat stopped at Shunyao, the Jesuits were met by a group of Buddhist monks who greeted them happily and insisted that they come to worship, and possibly stay, at their monastery. Matteo responded graciously and agreed to visit, but was wary—he now understood that some Chinese people preferred to be polite rather than honest.

They were taken on horseback to the Buddhist monastery, called Nanhua, in a green, fertile river valley. Once inside the temple, Matteo watched as the monks bowed to carved stone representations of their deities.

"This is idolatry!" whispered Antonio with shock.

"Yes, you are right. Let's leave as soon as we can."

The monks seemed to expect Matteo and Antonio to bow to the stone carvings. As politely as they could, the Jesuit priests declined and departed quickly, and hurried back to the junk that awaited them on the river.

"We will settle in Shaozhou—it is less than 200 miles from here," said Matteo to Antonio as they neared the boat. "There is no gain for us in having anything further to do with Buddhists."

In a few days, the ancient city of Shaozhou came into sight and Matteo was surprised by how happy he felt. Missionary hope once again filled his heart. Maybe here he would establish a lasting foothold—it was said to be a city of great culture and education.

Soon after settling into temporary quarters, both Matteo and Antonio became ill with a fever. Doctors came to care for the two men, treating them with traditional herbs and medicines. The priests were so weak they could only lie in their beds. After five days, the fevers subsided and they thanked God.

We are so vulnerable here, thought Matteo of how ill he'd been. *I was so willing to depend on the Chinese doctors, even though the medicines they used were completely unknown to me.*

Good news arrived as Matteo recovered: The governor of the province decided to grant him land at no cost on which to build a modest residence. Matteo felt as if he'd been given a new life, and with great enthusiasm began to design the space and ask about competent builders in the city.

It didn't take long for visitors to come knocking on the door. Scholars and educated men from wealthy families came from afar to visit. The poor found their way to the Jesuit residence too.

They'd heard about the tall European with dark, sad eyes who wore robes of silk—was he a magician?

They'd heard he had great knowledge of mathematics and astronomy. Would he speak—in Mandarin!—about the stars and the sun?

They'd heard he wanted to tell them all about his foreign god.

They'd heard he had a mechanical object that rang by itself throughout the day, and that he had a map of the world. Where did he come from and why was he here?

Most of all they wanted a chance to study Matteo's mannerisms and his strange, long face. Never had they been in the presence of stranger like him.

Matteo obliged. He was used to being stared at and receiving a barrage of questions from Chinese visitors. He knew how to bow and graciously answer each one, no matter how simple. It was a great benefit that he could speak to them fluently and without hesitation. He also knew they would eventually ask about his religion, and he was eager to explain to them—particularly to the literati, who were educated—the teachings of Jesus, the stories of the Bible, and how he came to his own faith, in terms they could easily understand.

So many people arrived at their doorstep every day that Matteo asked one of the servants to keep a record of all their names. One name began to appear on the list regularly: Qu Taisu.

"Who is he?" Matteo asked the servant.

"I have heard that he once was firmly on the path to become a government official," he replied. "But when his father died, he inherited a great fortune and he abandoned that path."

"Very interesting. So he is an educated man, a Confucian," said Matteo thoughtfully. "Does he have a wife and family?"

"His wife died many years ago, and gave him no children. His concubine has remained with him."

Matteo's curiosity was piqued and he sent an invitation to the man to visit the following day for tea. Qu Taisu arrived early. He was short in stature with long black hair and a broad face that broke into a bright smile. At the entrance of the residence, he bowed down three times and then offered gifts: a basket of food and a piece of wood carved into the shape of a mountain and river.

"Father Ricci, I ask to be your disciple," he said, looking down at the floor.

Taken by surprise, Matteo was not sure how to answer.

Qu Taisu continued. "I have visited this residence many times to see your treasures, and have heard you speak about them."

"I would be honored to discuss this possibility," Matteo said to Qu Taisu kindly. "What is it you wish to learn?"

"I have heard that you know how to turn plain metal into silver."

Matteo sighed. Ah, yes, this reputation for alchemy and magic had followed him. But he wasn't about to spurn this opportunity.

"I will teach you something far more useful and powerful: mathematics."

Qu Taisu tilted his head in question. He bowed and said, "As you wish. I invite you to come to my home for a banquet that befits your great knowledge."

"I would be delighted," said Matteo.

"It is my honor, and I eagerly await your visit—and our first lesson."

As Qu Taisu turned and left the residence, Matteo watched

in amazement. God was most certainly opening a door, but where would it lead?

As Matteo stepped into Qu Taisu's house later that week, he glimpsed a woman peering at him from around the corner of a back wall. She appeared to be young with bright dark eyes. Matteo immediately sensed that she was suppressing a giggle at the sight of him. But before he could say hello, she disappeared behind the wall. Could this be Qu Taisu's concubine?

Qu Taisu stepped forward and invited Matteo in. The house was small, well built, and impeccably clean. They sat formally across from each other at a low table, where small bowls of steaming soup awaited them. Matteo delicately inquired about his host's life, and learned that Qu Taisu was forty years old, just three years older than Matteo. In his own home, Qu Taisu was now more relaxed and spoke easily.

"I come from a very rich, well-known family, Father, and I attended the best schools. But in the last ten years, I have been reckless and now I am reduced to poverty," he said. "I gave most of my money away to men so that they would teach me the tricks of alchemy—to no gain. I wandered through many provinces and committed an act which caused my family disgrace." He lowered his eyes. "I fell in love with my sister-in-law, and we . . . ."

Matteo said nothing, waiting for Qu Taisu to continue.

"Now, I have only a few servants, and I live on gifts I receive from men who remember my father. They loved him and they love me because I am his son. The great government official—yes, my father was a man everyone admired. But, Father Ricci, I can tell you, he was not so kind to his own family. He was cold and strict with me, so much that I refused to speak to him or to apply myself to my studies. My father wanted me to be like him, yet I was determined I would be as different as I could!"

Matteo studied Qu Taisu. Clearly he was well spoken and educated, despite his simple way of dressing and the humble home. He seemed almost playful and didn't take himself too seriously.

Qu Taisu studied Matteo just as intently. He was fascinated by this foreign monk's quiet, thoughtful demeanor and genuine friendliness. He noted melancholy in Matteo's eyes and wondered, *Why has he come so far away from his home?*

"I can teach you mathematics and astronomy," said Matteo. "And if you pay attention and remember every lesson, you will gain more knowledge in these subjects than anyone in China."

Is he exaggerating? Qu Taisu sensed he was not, and readily agreed.

Within a few days, Matteo arranged for him to move into a room in the Buddhist monastery where the Jesuits had taken up temporary residence. Their daily lessons would begin immediately.

Unlike many other Chinese men Matteo had met, Qu Taisu was open-minded and independent in his thinking. He was eager to know about Matteo's background and education and was ready to take on difficult lessons in mathematics and astronomy.

Matteo was fluent in Mandarin, so he could teach Qu Taisu easily, but what if other Chinese wanted to be his students? It would be much easier if he had a text written in Chinese. Watching Qu Taisu struggle over mathematics problems, Matteo was reminded how much Euclid's *Elements of Geometry* had helped him when he was a student. *I need to translate that book into Chinese,* he thought. He knew he could do it, and that it would take years, but he silently vowed to begin as soon as possible.

It wasn't long before he was also instructing Qu Taisu on Christian morality and doctrines, including the transforming power of forgiveness. Qu Taisu was intensely curious and asked many questions: Why did Matteo's Christian god seem to have human characteristics? What did Christians say about good and evil?

Qu Taisu explained Confucianism. "Kindness in relationships is very important," he said, noting how carefully Matteo listened. "The five relationships are sovereign and subject, older and younger, husband and wife, parent and child, friend and friend. Each relationship connects us to another person, and we must show sympathy and good will to the other."

Matteo knew there was another common relationship in China: man and concubine. He gently encouraged his student to convert to Christianity, but Qu Taisu knew he would have to give up his concubine or marry her—and he was not ready to do either.

Chapter Twelve

CONFUCIAN ROBES

Deep within the strange lands and customs of China, the Jesuits found comfort in their familiar routine of prayer and meditation. Naturally they spoke Italian among themselves and sang simple hymns in Latin. They recited parts of the Bible and praised God's goodness and mercy for their continued survival.

They needed this daily spiritual sustenance. Their walks through the surrounding neighborhoods brought them in contact with men and women—if only they could simply speak to them. Some people turned and ran away in fear at the sight of the Jesuits, others angrily shouted at them to leave, and still others threatened them with sticks and rocks. Evangelizing was not easy work, and the Jesuits tried to keep their spirits up as best they could. Despair, like self-pity, was to be avoided.

But Matteo had another, more urgent worry.

His trusted Jesuit companion, Antonio de Almeida, had become severely weakened by his extreme ascetic practices—he even deprived himself of food. He sometimes could not even go out with the others on the daily outings to evangelize. A Chinese priest, who had taken the name of Francisco Martins, tended to Antonio, but it was no use. Antonio wasn't getting better. The cuts he'd inflicted on himself never had a chance to heal. Matteo finally insisted that Francisco take Antonio to Macao, where he could be seen by a European doctor.

Soon after his return to Shaozhou a month later, Antonio, at the young age of thirty-four, succumbed to infection and died. Matteo deeply regretted that he hadn't tried harder to stop the young priest from his extreme behavior. He'd hoped Antonio would serve a long life as a missionary in China.

With a heavy heart he went through Antonio's belongings. He was surprised to find a small book, a diary. In it were written beautiful, poetic entries about his visions of God and revelations during the last few years of his spiritual journey. *Who should have this?* Matteo wondered as he held the soft, leather-bound book.

That evening he presented it to Francisco Martins. The Chinese priest nearly cried when he saw what it was, and thanked Matteo profusely. That night Matteo prayed for the soul of the deceased young man and that his spirit of devotion would be carried on in the others.

But the drama of Antonio's death was not over. The priests now faced a dilemma: Where to bury his body? Chinese law forbade burial near the church, yet Matteo could not allow this faithful priest to be buried on some faraway hillside. The preserved body was placed in a coffin at the back of the residence for two years until a local official allowed the Jesuits to send it to Macao for a proper burial.

Nothing is easy here, Matteo thought. It was hard not to feel bitter sometimes.

~

It was obvious to all the Jesuits living in Shaozhou that Qu Taisu, as a valuable friend and intermediary, could smooth the way to introductions with men of influence and power. He taught the priests proper Chinese etiquette for every social situation, which helped them avoid embarrassing mistakes.

When one local magistrate invited the Jesuits to a banquet, Matteo asked Qu Taisu to come along to assist with the formalities. As the evening progressed and the guests had indulged in good wine, Qu Taisu stood and recited a long poem, one he'd written himself that praised Matteo's many accomplishments— his scholarly studies, his sea travels, his sojourns in India and Macao, and his writings.

The officials listened with amazement, then turned and regarded the Italian priest with new respect as Qu Taisu sat down, smiling.

And so, with Qu Taisu's help, Matteo found his way into the inner circles of the influential Confucian scholars of Shaozhou, who were his intellectual equals, and from whom he had much to learn. He spoke with them about religion, often engaging in lively discussions. Matteo was eager to learn about the famous Four Books of Confucianism—Great Learning, Golden Mean, Analects, and Mencius. And he learned for the first time about the *I Ching*, or Book of Changes. It was an ancient text that contained hexagrams that some Chinese regarded as a kind of oracle. As he listened to the scholars eloquently describe their spiritual beliefs, Matteo wished that his friends from Rome could be there to hear it too.

An idea came to him: *I will translate the Four Books into Latin so that thousands of people in Europe will be able to read them.* He knew the Chinese would be elevated by the knowledge of Europeans, and he also believed the Europeans would benefit by being able to read the words of poets and learned men of China.

Matteo had found true friends among these educated men—like him, they revered literature, philosophy, art, and, of course, science. For the first time, he did not feel like a foreigner, or even an outsider. He began to construct in his mind a new kind catechism that would appeal to these literati.

And finally, at the urging of Qu Taisu—and with the blessing of Alessandro Valignano—he and the other Jesuits stopped dressing as Buddhist priests and began to wear the signature robes of Confucian scholars.

"The reputation and credit of the preachers of this holy doctrine, and to a certain extent the reputation of the law itself, depend on accommodating and acting externally like the Chinese," he wrote to friends in Rome. "And now we see how it is important, because until recently we have been behaving with external humility and were considered to be Buddhist monks; we were always treated as lowly sorts and nobodies, and could never establish connections with mandarins and other people of note. And now, with this transformation, we have established connection with them and are treated with much honor and courtesies."

But not everyone was glad to have the Jesuits in their midst.

Chapter Thirteen

THE ATTACK

The Chinese New Year was approaching in 1592, and the Jesuits discreetly decided to celebrate in their own way. Matteo placed a framed painting of the Madonna and Child on the altar of their small church, hoping that neighbors who visited would be moved by the Madonna's expression of pure maternal love. It certainly had meaning for him. He'd brought the painting all the way from Rome, and the face of the Madonna reminded him of his grandmother. She had always been loving toward him in that same open, natural way.

But when the men and women saw the painting on prominent display, they reacted with revulsion and fear.

What is this strange image with foreign-looking faces?

What are these religious men up to?

Why do they want everyone to see this picture?

The Jesuits had been outspoken in their condemnation of locals who practiced astrology and fortune-telling. This backfired—neighbors became angry thinking that the Jesuits wanted to force their foreign ideas and morality on others.

One night Matteo was awakened by the sound of men shouting outside his window. A gang of young men had surrounded the residence and were throwing stones at it. He got out of bed and ran outside, where his servants were already confronting the gang. Unafraid, the men continued to pick up sharp rocks and pelt the servants.

Francesco de Petris, a young priest who'd just arrived from Macao, was struck in the head. As Matteo ran toward him in the dark, he tripped and fell, crying out in agony—he'd twisted his ankle. The rock-throwers fled, and Matteo, hobbling, helped bring Francesco back inside.

As the servants pulled his thick dark hair aside to stop the bleeding from a head wound, Francesco asked with a laugh, "Father, is this how they welcome Jesuits in China?"

"No, no, my dear young man. The neighbors are suspicious at times, but nothing like this has ever happened," said Matteo as the pain shot up from his foot, which was quickly swelling. "Please, do not let this turn your mind against them. We are quite alien to them. Many of them conclude that because we are different than they are, we must be conspiring to do something evil."

Officials arrived the next day to investigate the incident, but Matteo waved them off, explaining that he forgave the perpetrators, that they simply misunderstood his purpose in Shaozhou.

Qu Taisu, watching Matteo, was incredulous. "You must not forgive these thugs," he said when the officials had left. "They—the officials, the neighborhood, the gang—will think you are weak if you do not bring charges against them. Father, they destroyed our property and they hurt you."

"I have reason for not bringing charges," Matteo insisted. "I need to ask permission for a travel permit for other priests to come here from Macao. If I ask for justice against these gang members, I cannot in the same breath ask for the travel permit. I would appear greedy."

"Leave this to me," said Qu Taisu. "I understand these nuances of etiquette and power more than you do."

In the next week, the culprits were caught, and a letter arrived asking Matteo how many travel permits he would need for the following months. Matteo did not ask how this all came about so swiftly.

Chapter Fourteen

RESPITE

Francesco de Petris raced across the cobblestone courtyard of the Jesuit residence and up the stairs to the door of Matteo's room, a letter from Italy in his hand.

Receiving a letter was a rare event and reason for excitement. Francesco had grown up in Rieti, Italy, and he was thrilled for Matteo, who opened his door and greeted the young priest. He took the letter with a big smile.

Francesco's enthusiasm for missionary work lightened the days for all the other priests in the small Jesuit residence. Sometimes he even broke into boisterous Italian country songs while he did his chores, making everyone laugh.

The young man's path to Shaozhou had been remarkably similar to Matteo's. The thirty-one-year-old had studied at the Roman College before sailing to Goa and then to Macao. He was strong, healthy, and eager to share the Gospel. He plunged into studying Chinese with Matteo—he wanted to learn it as quickly as he could so that he could do the missionary work he craved.

After thanking Francesco for the letter, Matteo turned to sit at his wooden desk where he could open it in private. It was from Father Alessandro Valignano, asking Matteo to come to Macao for a brief stay. Though he could still hardly walk because of his injured foot, Matteo immediately began preparing for the sea journey to Macao.

Two weeks later, as the boat entered the wide, crowded harbor of Macao, Matteo suddenly found himself straining to catch sight of the familiar streets. He'd desperately wanted to escape the city years before, but now his eyes filled with tears at the sight of the buildings and docks.

As soon as he could, he hobbled off the ship carrying one small bag, eager to get to the Jesuit community. When he approached the residence, Alessandro Valignano greeted him from an open door, calling his name.

"Matteo Ricci, you are here—our intrepid missionary! Come in and sit with me at once. I have a surprise for you."

"Father, it is a gift beyond measure to see you," said Matteo, and began to explain about the attacks in Shaozhou, when suddenly he saw a familiar face enter the room.

"Oliviero Toscanelli!" Matteo shouted and rushed to his old friend. The two men embraced. "Of course, you've been traveling with Father Valignano! How good to see you, my friend. Have you been back to Macerata? Rome? Tell me everything!"

"Please, please, before you start, let us have our lunch and some wine in the garden," said Alessandro. "We have much to tell each other!"

The three men spent weeks in Macao in the Jesuit residence there sharing their experiences. Alessandro and Oliviero described their journeys into Japan, and Matteo shared all his news from Zhaoqing and Shaozhou. He told them of the death of Antonio de Almeida, and how Francesco de Petris had eased some of the pain with his generous spirit. It was such a relief to be able to speak freely with these two men about the tremendous difficulties he'd faced.

"I'm afraid I hindered our progress by dressing as a Buddhist monk," he told them as the three men walked through the hills of Macao after dinner one evening. "The most respected men of the country are the literati, who are Confucian scholars. They influence the men of power—so in order to gain their recognition and respect, I changed my dress so that I appear to be one of them."

When his two friends looked at him quizzically, Matteo laughed.

"It is not very strange dress—simply a purple silk robe with a blue sash and silk shoes."

"Silk shoes! I wish I could see you dressed that way!" said Oliviero, laughing. Then after a few moments, he added, "My brother Matteo, what an extraordinary adventure you've embarked upon—I can only think of our beloved Francis Xavier. You walk in his spiritual footsteps with the same bravery that he had. I admire you for all you've done."

"But I have done so little!" Matteo cried out in frustration. "So few converts after all this time! True conversion takes much time and education, I understand that. So many of the poor people are hoping for some kind of magic that will make their hard lives suddenly better—in their cases, conversion is superficial and does not last. I am profoundly disappointed that we've made a mere eighty or so true converts."

Alessandro stopped and regarded Matteo kindly. It was now

dark, but the night air was warm and a pleasant breeze rustled in the trees along the path.

"By your work there, by living among the people, they have come to know you—and yes, you say that many are not accepting of you. Nonetheless, because they see you day in and day out, they know what a European man looks like, and that Jesuits are kind, faithful, and seekers of justice. This, my son, is a tremendous accomplishment with lasting consequences. Until now, most Chinese have never seen a European and you have singlehandedly made their world bigger. Your presence there will lead to many more converts in the future."

Matteo nodded at these generous words. "I must tell you both," he said, "that the continual hardship I've endured has caused me to question God's wish for me. The answer that has come to me is this: God is inviting me to imagine our mission in a bigger way."

Alessandro and Oliviero looked at Matteo intently as they all turned a corner to head back to the Jesuit residence. A few lanterns with flickering candles could be seen in the houses they passed. Families were preparing for bed.

"I need to reach the emperor himself, Wan-li. Or, as he is also known, the Son of Heaven," said Matteo as his friends listened in silence. "And not just meet him, but establish a relationship with him. It is the only way. If he can see us not as a threat, but as brothers, then we will be able to safely establish Jesuits in China and expand our work in years to come. Without his approval, we are just fighting small—often futile—battles."

"What do you know of the emperor?" asked Alessandro.

"It is a curious story," answered Matteo. "He has many talents—among them archery and calligraphy. In the first years of his reign, he followed the guidance of his mentor and secretary and worked diligently for the good of the people. He made wise military decisions and kept able men as his confidants. The country prospered as a result. But when his mentor died, Wan-li changed. His judgment suddenly evaporated."

"What was the cause?" asked Oliviero.

"Some say he simply went mad—he refuses to govern. Others say he is clashing with his own officials because he wants his son, born of a concubine, to succeed him. And another rumor is that he's become an opium fiend, that he takes the drug day and night . . . that his health and his mind are in a state of decline. He is a complete recluse."

"This is a dangerous state for everyone," said Alessandro.

"Indeed," agreed Matteo. "Powerful eunuchs have taken control of Wan-li's life. They are common criminals who now surround the emperor. They are known to be cruel, extracting bribes from everyone in Beijing."

"Matteo, you have my blessing to attempt to meet Wan-li," said Alessandro. "I have faith that you will find a way to achieve this goal. But I caution you to be very, very careful. You, more than anyone, will be viewed with great suspicion and hostility. One wrong step and you could be imprisoned."

On this solemn note, the three men returned to the residence.

It was a balm to his soul to see his Jesuit friends, and when Matteo returned to Shaozhou a month later, he felt restored and invigorated once again. It was February of 1593, and he was ready for the daunting challenges he knew lay ahead.

Chapter Fifteen

UNEXPECTED LOSS

The men who had attacked the Jesuit residence with rocks were hours away from execution. This was the first news Matteo received when he returned to Shaozhou.

He flew into action, writing to the officials pleading for leniency for the condemned men—he had no idea that the punishment would be death. After negotiating with the Jesuits, the officials finally released the perpetrators of the attack. But the next day, Matteo was mystified to learn that his neighbors were quite angry; they wanted to see the young attackers hang. He was glad he'd interrupted their bloodlust.

As he walked across the courtyard of the residence, he quietly made the sign of the cross on his chest, then stopped as he heard running behind him.

One of the servants ran into the courtyard. "Father, come quickly!"

Matteo turned and followed the servant as fast as he could, asking what was the matter.

"It's Father de Petris. He's very ill," said the servant.

"Yes, I know, he has a malaria fever, which he will recover from—why all of a sudden are you concerned?" Matteo was confused. He'd checked on Francesco just the evening before and his fever seemed to be holding steady. He had complete faith that the robust young man would be back on his feet in a day or two.

He now rushed into the room of the priest, who lay in bed, his face as pale as the sheets soaked in his sweat. Matteo knelt beside Francesco and grasped the hand of the sick young man whose dark hair was matted with perspiration.

"I'm sorry, Father," said Francesco, his eyes glistening in a strange way that disturbed Matteo. "I'm afraid my death will cause trouble for you."

"You are not dying, my son, fear not," said Matteo.

"But I am, Father, I know that I am," replied Francesco. "Allow me to confess to you."

Matteo nodded and closed his eyes as the young man made his confession. When he saw that Francesco had drifted into sleep, Matteo rose and left the room feeling deeply upset. The next day, he was not completely surprised when he learned that the young priest had died.

His heart was crushed by this unexpected death. He left the residence and began walking along a dirt path beside the river. The sight of the slow-moving brown water, the tree branches leaning lazily out over the rippling current, and the occasional passing boat soothed him immediately.

A bright young man, so full of hope and promise—Francesco, who exemplified the missionary spirit of Francis Xavier—was gone forever. *God, have you sent me here only to be attacked, to be a helpless witness of injustice, to watch good people die?*

He was angry with God. He couldn't help it. Matteo gazed at the water, then looked up at a black crow gliding above the trees. Words from Mark in the New Testament came to him: "For whoever wants to save his life will lose it, but whoever loses his life for My sake and for the Gospel will save it."

The loss of Francesco made him suddenly ache for his family in Macerata. He longed for stories of his family. He often dreamed of the streets of Macerata, the little shops he had passed every day as a child, the friendly neighbors who all knew his name, and the green fields where he and his siblings played at the edge of the city walls.

He'd written many times, but only a few letters reached him from his father. Upon returning to his room at the Jesuit house, Matteo sat down at his desk and found ink, a pen, and a rough paper on which to write a letter to his father in Italy. He paused for a moment, imagining his family gathered around to hear his words read aloud.

"For some years now I have not received news from home," Matteo wrote. "Either you have not written, or the letters are lost in transit; but I have not forgotten to remember you in my poor sacrifices. If it is not too much trouble, it would gladden me to know how you are and whether everyone is alive."

A year later, a letter arrived from Macerata. His father informed Matteo that his beloved grandmother, Laria, had died with his name on her lips. "*Diglielo, lo amo, non ho mai smesso di amare il mio caro nipote,*" she had said. Tell him I love him. I have never stopped loving my dear grandson. There was no other news of the family in the letter.

Matteo closed his eyes and repeated the words to himself. Laria had loved him more than anyone else in the world. He could almost feel the warmth of her wrinkled hand on his arm—

she would often touch his hand or face when speaking to him. The silver cross that hung around her neck came into his mind. How he had loved that cross, and the kind old woman who'd worn it.

Chapter Sixteen

BEIJING

Sun Kuang, the vice minister of war, hated not knowing what to do, and right now he felt helpless.

His only son, age twenty-two, was immobilized by depression and had even begun muttering to himself. No matter what the father said, it had no effect on the young man's strange moods. Sun Kuang had heard about the Jesuit priests in Shaozhou, that they possessed great knowledge about the stars, sun, and moon. Maybe they knew how to heal his son.

Matteo was surprised to receive a messenger bearing a message and gifts from Sun Kuang. They had never met. But the official was inviting him to visit as soon as possible. He wanted to discuss trouble with his son.

Having lost the relationship with his own father, Matteo was hopeful that he might be able to mend another father-son relationship.

Now Matteo was invited into the large, formal house of Sun Kuang, where he was led to a wide sitting room. Sun Kuang was a big man who spoke loudly when he introduced his son, a slim young man who sat sullenly looking out the window. Kuang explained that ever since his son had done poorly on his school exams, he had become immobilized with guilt or remorse—he didn't know which. The young man would not eat or speak, except to mumble to himself. At that moment, he yawned loudly as if to express his boredom, then put his head in his hands.

"I sat for many examinations," said Matteo, looking toward the son, "and sometimes I became sick with fear about whether or not I would do well."

The young man refused to give any sign that he was listening.

"But now," continued Matteo, "I understand that every person has talents and qualities that cannot be measured by an examination. The ability to love or to play music or to help someone who is weak, for instance."

The son looked up briefly and Matteo thought he saw tears.

"This is a big problem," said the father, "because I have been called to Beijing on an urgent matter, and I do not want to leave my son alone. Do you think you can help him, Father?"

Beijing? Matteo's heart skipped a beat. Suddenly he saw a chance to go directly to the Forbidden City—the vast Imperial Palace of Emperor Wan-li that had been built in 1420.

"Yes, I can. And I have a suggestion," replied Matteo. "Perhaps your son and I could accompany you to Beijing. That way I can talk to him over many days and we will always be close to you, should I need your help."

Sun Kuang looked at Matteo thoughtfully. "I run a great risk even speaking to you, a foreigner in our land. Accompanying me on a long trip may not be taken well by certain officials along the way."

Matteo nodded. He knew the situation.

"However, I need help for my son," Sun Kuang continued. "I will agree to this arrangement. You must be ready to leave early tomorrow morning—before dawn so that few people see you. You may bring four others with you, but little baggage. Do not be late."

Sun Kuang's son turned slightly, watching Matteo rise and then bow to them both. A small smile crossed his face as Matteo said goodbye.

Matteo invited two young Chinese catechists who had been living at the residence to join them on the journey. João Barradas and Domingo Fernandes were their early twenties and excited for an adventure that might take them all the way to Beijing. The next morning, they arrived with Matteo at the dock where several junks belonging to Sun Kuang and his entourage waited. It was May of 1595, and the river was full from the many springs that fed into it. They learned that they would have a small junk to themselves and that Sun Kuang's son would be traveling on this boat too. In the soft sunlight filtering through mist and clouds, the men boarded the small fleet of junks and set off for the long, meandering journey through rivers and canals.

Each day Matteo sat alone with Sun Kuang's son, asking him about his interests and engaging him in philosophical discussions, never once mentioning the disastrous exams. They watched as the boatman shifted the course of the junk safely up the river. Away from his father, who was with his servants on the largest junk of the fleet, the young man began talking freely, his mood brightening.

Matteo suggested that together they create a record of the journey, noting the weather, currents, and other boats. At night, he showed the young man how to identify constellations and planets. During the day, he explained how to use the astrolabe and calculate the latitudes of each village and town.

"I know that you are . . ." the young man hesitated as he spoke to Matteo one afternoon, ". . . from another country, far away. I am glad you came here—you are very kind. And . . . I would like to learn the way you learn. The way you teach, I feel happy. No pressure."

The skies had turned dark gray and a wind had picked up. The boatman was alert to the shift in the weather, though Matteo and the young man barely noticed.

"The kindness you feel comes from God, the God I have known all my life," said Matteo quietly. "As I have been forgiven, I forgive others. God forgives you too. And you can forgive yourself . . . and your father. This is my religion, my belief."

The priest and the young man now finally realized that the light wind had become stronger, buffeting the sails and making the water choppy.

Matteo stopped talking and nervously scanned the water. It was these moments when he regretted never learning how to swim—the boat did not seem strong enough to withstand a storm. Suddenly a powerful gust came out of nowhere and hit the sail, toppling the boat and tossing all the passengers into the strong river current. Matteo tried to grab the rail before he was swept into the cold rushing water, and soon he was sinking. With great effort he forced his way to the surface, gasping for air. He heard others shout for help, and he flailed helplessly and sank once again, the water carrying him swiftly downstream.

Heavenly Father, help me! The plea filled his mind as he felt himself sink once again. A bump against his shoulder stopped him—it was the capsized boat. He grabbed a rope that dragged from its side and pulled his body up. The boat was being pushed fast toward the river's edge. Blustering wind still pounded the water and two men on land strained to grab the boat and pull it in. Within minutes, Matteo lay on the ground, cold and soaking wet, as someone covered him with a blanket.

"The others—where are they?" he gasped.

"We have them all," said Domingo, "all . . . except João."

"We must save him!" said Matteo, throwing off the blanket. He got up and staggered along the shore, calling the young man's name, searching for some sign of him in the water. But he was gone.

That evening, as he and the other passengers gathered in a small inn in a village near the river, Matteo saw Sun Kuang enter, and he stood. The official signaled that he wanted to speak to Matteo alone and the two retreated to a low table near a fireplace.

"How is everyone? Your son?" Matteo asked.

"Our men, and my son, are all safe," said Sun Kuang with a grim expression. "This accident is a sign that I cannot continue my journey with you," he stated bluntly. "I have spoken with my son, and you have healed him. For this I am very thankful. But as a foreigner, you cannot travel further without explicit knowledge and approval of the emperor. It is too dangerous for all of us."

Matteo knew he could not argue with the big man, as illogical as he was, so he simply nodded. The fire cracked in the blackened stone fireplace.

"I recommend that you go back to Shaozhou immediately."

Matteo knew this was impossible, and said so.

Sun Kuang's face darkened with anger. "Then I direct you to go to Nanchang, the capital of the province. I know several men there who will welcome you and will give you letters of recommendation. You will find it is a peaceful city, suited to your temperament."

After saying goodbye to Sun Kuang and sending good wishes to his son, Matteo went to his room at the inn and fell into a deep and troubled sleep.

He was in the dark water, and by twisting his body he could see João a few feet away. He reached out, but João kept slipping further, just out of his grasp. João turned his head and seemed to wave goodbye. Matteo tried to shout, but no sound came out. He pulled himself to the surface of the water and suddenly awoke, sitting up in his bed, breathing fast.

He looked wildly around his room, then lowered his head in his hands and wept.

Chapter Seventeen

FAME IN NANCHANG

The next morning, Matteo and Domingo talked about their predicament: turn back or keep going? Domingo, shaken by the loss of his friend, was determined to continue on to Beijing, and offered to find a boat to hire so that they could continue north.

Matteo admired the young priest's determination, which matched his own. By the afternoon, Domingo had secured a boat, and the solemn group, grieving the loss of João Barradas, was underway toward that city.

Matteo and Domingo watched the passing landscape together—vast green fields interrupted by small towns, pagodas, and buildings with curved roofs, sitting on the banks of the river. Matteo could see villagers in markets selling fresh produce and asked the boat to stop so that he and his companions could buy some food for the journey.

He regretted it immediately.

Crowds of people came running to the dock at the sight of

him, a strange-looking foreigner. Some tried to grab at his clothing and shouted at him in a mix of curiosity, excitement, and fear. Matteo escaped and jumped back on the boat, calling out to the boatman to push off quickly. He vowed that from then on, he would try to stay out of sight.

He also wanted travel north as quickly as they could.

It was early morning when the boat entered the great Lake Poyang, which covered nearly 1,400 square miles and was fed by several large rivers. Porpoises swam swiftly beneath the water's surface and flocks of birds swooped over the marshes. The boatman expertly navigated through the hundreds of other boats without bumping into any of them, making his way through the currents, continuing north toward the wide Yangtze River.

After many weeks, they reached the city of Nanking.

The men were intrigued at the great city wall with its large, intimidating gates. Surely no enemies would get through without being seen by guards. The streets, lined with plane trees that reminded them of Europe, seemed to overflow with markets, and brightly colored temples dotted the hills. Gently rising above the city was Zijin Shan, or the Purple Mountain.

Matteo knew one person here—a mandarin he'd met in Shaozhou—and hoped he could find him. Wearing clothing of a Confucian scholar and his beard now long and streaked with gray, Matteo knew he stood out in the crowd. He quickly hired a covered litter so that he could keep his face hidden behind its curtains.

He located the home of his scholar friend with little trouble, and the man welcomed him in, inviting Matteo to stay while he found a permanent residence. But within hours, word of the Jesuit's presence had spread. A government official suddenly appeared at the door.

"You, foreigner, cannot stay here," said the official. "You do not have permission. You must leave immediately."

"But where can we go?" asked Matteo, genuinely unsure of what to do.

"Go back south to Nanchang," said the official, looking down, as if he did not want to appear to be helpful. "It will be easier for you there."

Matteo realized that his very presence put his friend in danger, and was angry with himself for not obtaining official permission to visit. The official kept watch just outside the house until Matteo at last departed to return to the boat.

When he convened with the other Jesuits, they agreed there was no choice but to go back to Nanchang. As they watched the city and the Purple Mountain recede, their mood was somber.

It was early June. Irritated by the constant heat and discouraged by the official rejection, Matteo found a bunk into which he fit his long body, and closed his eyes to rest. He fell into a deep sleep, in which he had a dream.

He was walking on a long, dusty road when a stranger wearing old, torn clothing and no shoes approached him. The stranger questioned him loudly. "Is your intention here to extinguish the ancient religions and replace it with a new one?"

In the dream, Matteo turned to this stranger, surprised and irritated by the question. "To know about this, you must be God—or the Devil. Who are you?" he asked.

The stranger replied mysteriously, "I am not the Devil."

Matteo froze, then fell to the man's feet. "If you know what I am trying to do, why do you not help me?" he asked quietly.

In the dream, the stranger, whom Matteo now understood to be God, reached out to console him. At once, Matteo knew that his journey ahead was blessed and guided by the Holy Ghost.

~

Three years later, in 1598, he was sailing northward on the Gian Jing River, a southern tributary of the Yangtze River. He was with an official, a young man named Wang Zhongming, who'd agreed to help him meet with the emperor. It seemed almost too good to be true.

Wang Zhongming was educated and had an open, curious mind, and he very much respected Matteo's learning. He had been planning a trip to Beijing to participate in the celebrations of the thirty-fifth birthday of the emperor. When Matteo offered to pay for his own passage as well as for two of his Jesuit brothers, Wang Zhongming readily agreed. They had boarded a large junk with their many treasures from Europe, which they kept carefully wrapped and hidden.

I am closer than ever to fulfilling the dreams of Francis Xavier, thought Matteo with secret excitement. The Imperial Palace was called the Forbidden City because only the emperor, his family, servants, and the guards who lived there were allowed into the compound. Outside visitors were not allowed unless invited by the emperor.

Matteo had heard descriptions of the vast structure with 9,999 rooms built on a north-south line. The palace was known for its wide courtyards, gardens, and halls. Every detail of its architecture had been designed with symbolic meaning.

As Matteo gazed across the calm river before him, he reflected on the past few years and the happy life in Nanchang that he had just left.

"Oh ye of little faith," he said out loud with a laugh, remembering how dejected he'd felt when he and his companions were forced to leave Nanking and take up residence in Nanchang.

Nanchang . . . his life and missionary work had flourished in that city.

"The people are better; they look better, they are more noble, there are more literati, and the people are more courteous and considerate," he'd written of Nanchang to his friends in Rome. It was certainly a welcome contrast to the humiliation and attacks at Zhaoqing and Shaozhou. He'd met many fine, educated men and had written a book about friendship that became very popular among them.

Nanchang was a bustling center of trading activity, so Matteo's reputation as a man of religion and science had reached the officials as well as the wealthy men of the city long before he arrived. Within days of stepping out onto the streets of Nanchang, Matteo began to receive invitations to banquets given by high-ranking men and literati. Soon he found himself going out every night to dinners where singers and musicians provided entertainment and guests enjoyed continuous dishes of food and drink, along with boisterous conversation, for hours.

One nobleman named Prince Kang Yi was so intrigued by the foreign priests that he donated money so that they could work and study in peace. The prince was fascinated by their knowledge, their humble way of living, and Matteo's fluency in the Mandarin language.

He and the others were dumbfounded at the priest's ability to recite long poems in Chinese—his memory was extraordinary. They besieged him with questions about Christianity. *What is*

*this item he called a crucifix, and what does it symbolize? And who
is this mother with a baby who is depicted in the painted icons?*

Secretly, they were also intrigued by his celibacy. This man
never took a concubine.

Matteo was well aware that he was the object of their constant scrutiny, that in a sense he was an ambassador for all of
Europe and all of Christianity. He chose his words carefully
when he spoke of God, Jesus, the Virgin Mary, and the crucifix,
hoping he could explain everything in a way that the Chinese
could comprehend.

And he had questions of his own: *Do you believe in heaven
and hell? Do the principles of yin and yang extend to your understanding of astronomy?* His hosts, after several glasses of wine,
were happy to talk well into the night.

They admired this foreigner, but did not understand him.

"I have met him three times already and still do not know
his intentions in coming here," said Li Zhi, a well-known Confucian writer, to another guest.

"No, it is not clear," said the other man. "He seems to enjoy
our company. He tells us about his ideas of God, but he seems
to have no desire to dominate."

"Yes, I see that too," commented a third dinner guest. "And
he has read the classics and dresses like a Confucian scholar,
though he calls himself a Jesuit, a Christian. It's very confusing—but I like him."

Matteo was pleased to be welcomed at the banquets and he
was deeply gratified by the friendships he was slowly beginning
to make among the scholarly men. It had been a long time since
he'd felt appreciated rather than shunned.

Late at night, after he'd returned to the Jesuit residence, he
looked out of his window at the moon.

The same moon that his father could see in the Italian sky.

The same moon that his friends in Rome could ignore as they walked home from their meetings.

The same moon that Francis Xavier had gazed at years before, when he plotted his missionary path to China.

All his life, Matteo felt most understood by his friends—they knew and accepted him more than his father, mother, or siblings. Only his grandmother Laria provided that complete, loving acceptance he felt from his friends.

His childhood friends in Macerata, his beloved student friends in Rome, his fellow missionaries—they had loved him, cheered him, and sustained him throughout the best and worst times. He was moved to realize that in this strange and often cold country, he had found true friends in the intellectual elite. With their friendship, his heart opened and the loneliness disappeared.

What was the essence of a true friendship? He thought back on his studies of Seneca, Cicero, and Plutarch and their wisdom about friendship.

"Mutual need and mutual support are the reasons to make friends," he wrote down now on a piece of rough paper at his desk. In friendships, no one was higher or lower than the other; friends were equal.

He'd seen bonds between noblemen in China that were so strong that they would do anything to help their friends' families. He wrote: "A devoted son will keep the friends that his father has made just as he inherits his father's wealth."

Remembering the official who dismissed him in Shaozhou, he wrote: "Friends and enemies are like music and noise, which are distinguished only by harmony or a lack thereof. Harmony is therefore the basis of friendship. With harmony, slight things grow to greatness. With discord, great things shrivel and fail."

Matteo enjoyed this collection of simple truths, each an aspect of friendship. He would make them into a book and dedicate it to Prince Kang Yi, who had supported the Jesuit residence. The title, he decided, would be *On Friendship, One Hundred Maxims for a Chinese Prince.*

After many months, the little book was done and Matteo found a printer who was able to produce several copies. Matteo gave them as gifts to his scholar friends, who excitedly shared them with others. Prince Kang Yi sent word that he found the book delightful and thanked Matteo for the honor. It was the first work written in Mandarin by a Westerner, and because of this, Matteo was soon known to many men who had never met him.

Once they did meet the famous Jesuit priest, they were even more impressed. Matteo's astounding memory captivated his new acquaintances. His banquet hosts begged him to demonstrate how he could memorize texts and poems after looking them over just once.

Matteo obliged at these parties, but he did not want to encourage the idea that he was performing magic. He explained that he had studied memorization techniques recorded by Latin and Greek writers, and from them, devised his own. He imagined a building with many rooms, and associated words with people or objects in each of these rooms. The literati clamored to learn more about this technique. Matteo wrote *The Treatise on Mnemonic Arts* in Mandarin for his many hosts.

But it was the solar eclipse of September 22, 1596, that sealed Matteo's reputation as a man of knowledge. Several weeks before, at one of the banquets he often attended, he described to his guests how it was possible to predict the next solar eclipse—and then proceeded to tell them how he had already calculated when the next one would occur. The guests listened with rapt attention, but were privately doubtful.

In two weeks, the sky eerily darkened on exactly the date and time Matteo had predicted. It was indeed the solar eclipse he had told his hosts about. He wrote to General Claudio Acquaviva in Rome, telling him how embarrassed he was by the sudden attention he received for this prediction, which any capable astronomer could have done. Visitors knocked on his door day and night, asking to see his instruments and peppering him with questions. Matteo and the other priests made every effort to be gracious and provide answers, but they were exhausted.

Alessandro Valignano was, of course, told of Matteo's flourishing reputation, and understood its tremendous advantage in his missionary work. The more people were able to see the great benefits of scientific knowledge, the more they would be drawn to Matteo's Christianity. Alessandro wrote to the Jesuits in China announcing that he intended to bestow upon Father Matteo Ricci the title of Superior of China.

Matteo hadn't expected this, but he was deeply grateful when he learned of this honor. It meant he had the official directive to oversee the residences that he had established in Shaozhou and Nanchang.

But more significantly, this title might just help him to gain a meeting with Emperor Wan-li.

Alessandro also sent a large wooden box filled with delicate treasures wrapped in layers of heavy cloth: a small harpsichord, a mechanical clock, numerous pieces of Venetian glass, fabrics threaded with gold. They were to be given as gifts to officials as Matteo made his way to Beijing.

Praise the Lord! Matteo thought as he ran his hands lovingly over each object. It was a miracle that they'd arrived in

Nanchang safely without a scratch. They greatly increased his chances of making it to the Forbidden City in Beijing where he might meet the emperor—a treacherous journey, most certainly. Gifts and bribes would be necessary along the way.

All these memories of Nanchang made Matteo smile as he gazed at the placid Yangtze River with its high green banks.

Now he was beginning a new adventure. He turned away from the serene view and went below deck to stretch out on his bunk. He was traveling with that box of treasures stowed safely nearby. Though the bed was hard and not very comfortable, Matteo knew he would sleep. He had all that he needed—a sturdy junk; the guidance of Wang Zhongming, who would take him to Beijing; the gifts; and the blessing of his beloved Father Alessandro Valignano. Several young Jesuit priests formed his little group, among them Lazaro Cattaneo from Sarzana, Italy, an area between Genoa and Florence. Surely, nothing could go wrong.

He awoke with a start at the sound of shouting voices on deck. Matteo leaped out of bed and ran up to see what was happening. The junk had been overtaken by an official vessel; its captain was onboard speaking to Wang Zhongming.

The captain turned and pointed at Matteo, looking him up and down as if he were a criminal. "And so here he is! This is the foreigner we've heard about." He glared at Wang Zhongming. "What business does he have with you?"

"He is traveling with gifts for the Emperor Wan-li. His intentions are pure. He is a friend."

"Is that so?" said the captain in a sarcastic tone. "And what about you? What are your intentions?"

"I have a home there and I am now returning to celebrate the birthday of our emperor," Wang Zhongming replied steadily.

"Very well. I'm going to leave you, but I advise you to proceed with caution. Spies are everywhere in our land, in all disguises. Watch out for them!"

And with that, the captain returned to his own boat, which heaved off.

Wang Zhongming was distressed. "I cannot be seen with you, Father," he said, looking at Matteo, anguish in his voice. "I cannot jeopardize my ability to travel freely to Beijing. But I cannot abandon you either. From here on, I will travel by land on horseback while you continue on this junk. Our journeys will be parallel and we can meet at my home in the city."

Matteo could only agree. He did not want to endanger Wang Zhongming, his only guide.

Ever the cartographer, Matteo studied the passing scenery, continually noting the distances between towns and villages, estimating the size of the fields and the height of the mountains as the junk sailed northward.

At last the boatman entered the Grand Canal—a large man-made waterway that ran north to south—and through a series of linked waterways connected to the Yangtze River. The Grand Canal enabled barges and junks filled with goods and merchandise of every kind to travel from southern cities all the way north to Beijing. Built many centuries before Matteo traveled it, the canal was continually being repaired and improved.

The Jesuits sailed on the Grand Canal for weeks. Eventually they observed more people along the water's edge—families who lived on boats had pulled to the shore to buy food at the markets. Instead of the open fields they'd seen for days, they now passed long stretches of low, sturdy houses. In September, three months after they'd set out, the Jesuits caught sight of Beijing.

On the evening of September 8, the feast day of the Virgin Mary, they disembarked at last, carrying their belongings and the heavy box of gifts onto land. Matteo looked around and took a deep breath.

"It's certainly colder here," he said, rubbing his hands together. "And the air is dry and dusty."

At that moment, the young priest Lazaro sneezed loudly, making them all laugh. They stopped a passing cart drawn by two men, and paid them to take their group toward the capital.

They were exhilarated to finally be on land and could not wait to reach the city. Soon the tall, thick outer walls came into view. Soldiers standing along the top holding long spears eyed them with menace. Matteo and the others looked around in wonder.

After they passed through one of the seven gates of the outer wall, they saw an inner wall that was more than thirty feet high and could be passed through by way of one of nine gates. Deep, hard ruts on the road made travel difficult and slow.

Matteo took in the scene with all his senses. The streets looked much poorer and bleaker than he expected. A powerful smell of horse manure filled his nostrils—it was everywhere, yet no one seemed to notice. The sound of horses clopping by was cut by a harsh whistling of the wind. The Jesuits said nothing, but each of them felt the same disappointment. Where was the splendor of Beijing that they had heard about?

Lazaro sneezed again, but this time his friends didn't laugh.

A small breeze kicked up dust into the dry air, and the smell of burning coal was now mixed into it. The faces of the people around them were covered with dust, filling every wrinkle and dulling their hair. The unpleasant scene reminded Matteo of a story—he once heard a man say that all the trees had been chopped down north of Beijing so that they could be used as fuel for its large population. Now he saw that it was true, and it was certainly the cause of the dust.

The Jesuits searched the streets of Beijing for lodging. They found a small inn, and the old innkeeper reluctantly gave them rooms, eyeing them suspiciously.

The next day, Matteo led them all to the home of Wang Zhongming, who welcomed them, glad to see that they had arrived safely. But once they were all seated at a low table and were given cups of tea, he shared bad news.

"I arrived two days ago, and regretfully have not been able to secure approval for you to stay here," he said.

Matteo's heart sank—he did not have a good feeling about this.

"I am sorry, but you see, the eunuchs in the palace demand many bribes, even for the smallest favor," said Wang Zhongming. "They not only guard the palace; they dominate the entire city and they are used to getting what they want."

Matteo nodded. He now knew about the eunuchs. They ran every aspect of the Imperial Palace, deciding who could enter and who could not, who was in favor and who should be punished. The emperor was unreliable, mostly due to constant opium use. Instead of governing, he had turned over most of his power to the eunuchs, though he still maintained ultimate control.

In the following days, Matteo ventured out to the streets looking for the mandarins who'd been recommended to him by friends, hoping to make their acquaintance. He began to realize how naïve he'd been to think that by luck one of them would help him gain access to the emperor. The usual welcome he received from learned men was not to be found. After opening their doors and seeing Matteo, these men of status backed away with a look of nervous fear. They quickly shut their doors with barely a word.

The streets were littered with garbage, and scrawny stray cats meowed hungrily. Passersby rarely exchanged greetings and many looked poor and downcast. Most distressing to Matteo was to see young men and women offering themselves as prostitutes in the shadows of the filthy streets.

"This city is a veritable Babylon of confusion," wrote Matteo to Alessandro Valignano, "full of all kinds of sins, with no one interested in justice, piety, or his own salvation."

How does anyone get in to see the emperor? Matteo wondered. He heard a story about two Muslim men from Arabia who'd arrived in Beijing the year before. They brought with them two lions as a gift to the emperor, who, in appreciation, granted them permission to stay and live there.

The gifts he'd brought were small and insignificant compared to live beasts.

By November, dejected and running out of money, the Jesuits knew it was time to leave.

Chapter Eighteen

REGROUPING

For the second time, Matteo's attempt to establish himself in Beijing was unsuccessful.

The weather turned bitterly cold soon after Matteo and his companions departed the city. Within a week the forty-six-year-old Jesuit developed a deep and painful cough. Since most of the Grand Canal was beginning to freeze, the group continued traveling back south on horseback through rice paddies and tea plantations, now partially covered in snow.

Once they arrived in Linqing, Matteo insisted that Lazaro and the others split off to find their own lodging, and to take the mechanical clock and other treasures with them for safekeeping. The snow blew down on the men under a heavy gray sky, and Matteo explained that he would journey on to the home of his friend Qu Taisu, who lived nearby. Lazaro watched with concern as Matteo turned his tired horse and disappeared into the snowstorm.

Qu Taisu was surprised and delighted to see Matteo, and

brought his shivering and sick friend into his home, immediately giving him a comfortable bed and a bowl of hot rice. He listened as Matteo recounted the disastrous trip to Beijing and then insisted his friend try to sleep. While Matteo slept, Qu Taisu paced around his house and stared out at the wintery landscape, thinking and plotting. Clearly Father Ricci's approach to Beijing had been all wrong.

He may be wise and knowledgeable, and he has lived in China for many years, thought Qu Taisu, *but Father Ricci is not equipped to navigate the treacherous army of eunuchs that surrounds an emperor who cares nothing about anyone but himself.* A strategy was needed and allies had to be established—officials and literati who already knew of Matteo's reputation—who would vouch for him and secure him the permission he needed to go back.

And yes, somehow the eunuchs would have to be dealt with.

Qu Taisu resolved to do everything he could to get Father Ricci back to Beijing and into the Forbidden Palace.

As soon as Matteo regained his strength, a familiar melancholy descended upon him. Though the air was bitingly cold, he went outside to walk in Qu Taisu's garden, where trees and bushes were bent with snow. In his mind, he went over every detail of the disastrous trip to Beijing. He did not want to indulge in self-pity. It was much more important to understand why that trip had gone so wrong. After this short morning walk, Matteo reentered the house and sat with Qu Taisu before a warm fire his host had made.

"It was terrible in Beijing," Matteo told his friend. "I was shunned by the men who usually welcome me, or who are at least curious to know more about me. It was as if I were bad luck."

"Li Madou, if I may say this—you were naïve," Qu Taisu said, using Matteo's chosen Chinese name. He handed his friend another bowl of rice. "Emperor Wan-li is irrational and violent. You are a foreigner—which is to say, an enemy. Without the emperor's approval to be there, you were in grave danger. And anyone seen with you would also be in danger. When the emperor is angry or feels slighted, people die. He cares about lavish gifts and taking whatever he desires. His treachery is facilitated by the eunuchs, who carry out their own violence. And these eunuchs are everywhere in the city."

Matteo listened quietly as his friend spoke.

"The emperor has nothing to say about the corruption that has infected every part of the government," Qu Taisu continued. "He forces the poorest men to work in mines while their families languish."

Matteo now understood the immense fear that had made people so unfriendly in Beijing.

"He is obsessed with pearls and he has put his eunuchs in charge of divers along the coasts," Qu Taisu added. "Divers are forced to bring in a monthly quota of pearls for Emperor Wan-li. If they don't meet the quota, they are tortured."

Then Qu Taisu lowered his voice as if he were afraid someone was listening. "Have you heard the name Ma Tang?"

Matteo shook his head.

"He is the most powerful and violent man in this region, a eunuch who has terrorized merchants and officials for many years. We must try to avoid him, but if we must face him, we must have elaborate gifts for him."

Qu Taisu convinced Matteo to travel back north to Nanking with him, where they would establish strategic relationships with high-ranking officials and bolster support for his journey to Beijing. Matteo saw immediately that his friend was right, and the two quickly prepared to leave for Nanking.

They entered the city walls just in time for New Year's celebrations in January of 1599. Families and friends flocked to the temples and gathered afterward for open-air banquets and music shows. They decorated their homes with red lanterns and colored ribbons, and every night for two weeks, fireworks exploded above the city for all to enjoy.

A local nobleman invited Matteo and Qu Taisu to stay with him until they located a residence of their own. He was an elderly man who insisted on showing them his private garden. Though deeply tired and longing for sleep, Matteo and Qu Taisu politely agreed to see the garden.

They were not prepared for its magnificent and serene beauty. A narrow path with many twists and turns wound around little hills made of rocks, pavilions, and waterfalls. Matteo and Qu Taisu spent more than an hour with their host, exploring the pathways and admiring the exotic trees and shrubs until the sun went down. Such gardens fascinated Matteo, who constantly compared them to the Italian gardens of his childhood town of Macerata. The climate was quite different in northern China, and only rarely did he recognize a flower or tree.

At last the men returned to the house. Matteo was grateful to avoid the street—it was difficult for him to get anywhere without being recognized and stopped. He was constantly approached by adults and children who pulled at his robes, asking him to speak Mandarin or to recite a poem by heart, and would burst into laughter to hear the foreigner speak their language. Some had heard he could turn plain metal into silver and demanded that he do his magic right there in front of them.

As usual, when Matteo and Qu Taisu had located a house to call their Jesuit residence, scientists, students, and scholars wearing their signature robes began to appear at the door, eager to meet the man who had created a world map with Chinese notations, had predicted a solar eclipse, and had written two texts in their language. Matteo greeted each visitor with courtesy. And as he did in every house in which he and his companions lived, Matteo put all his astronomy instruments, mechanical clocks, and Christian icons on display for visitors to see and touch.

Spring arrived, and Matteo was delighted to see that the warm sunshine made the plum trees bloom. He was also surprised when a group of young visitors asked if he would be their teacher. Soon he began giving informal lessons at the Jesuit residence in mathematics, geography, and astronomy.

One afternoon, a student lingered after class. "Father, you know we have some understanding of astronomy," he said with a smile.

"Yes, I do know this. And I am always interested to share knowledge," replied Matteo.

"Well, Father, have you visited the Imperial Observatory nearby?" asked the student.

Matteo's eyes lit up. Had he heard correctly?

"An observatory?"

"Yes," the student replied, and offered to bring his teacher to see it.

That evening, the two walked for a long distance to an area just outside the city called Jiming Hill. There, Matteo was amazed to see the old structure filled with astronomical instruments cast in bronze with sophisticated detail. His mind was reeling. Matteo had assumed that the Chinese astronomers had only a rudimentary knowledge of the stars, planets, and universe—had he been wrong all this time to assume that European knowledge was superior to that of the Chinese? Were their scientists just as informed?

With intense interest, he examined the dusty instruments and discovered they were not properly calibrated. He politely asked the students why, and they admitted to having no idea how to use them. Matteo nodded. Now he understood—the astronomers who'd made the instruments had not passed on their knowledge before they died. He resolved that he would teach these students everything he knew.

Matteo's life in Nanking—with the banquets, lessons, and meetings with the literati—was enjoyable, and at times even amusing, but his Jesuit brothers knew him well and could sense his growing agitation. The year was passing quickly, and he wanted to return to Beijing.

Until that could happen, he continued to respond to the questions of his dinner hosts. One day a Buddhist monk angrily challenged his beliefs. Matteo had no fear of verbal sparring—in fact, he relished it. After all, he had mastered debate as a teenager, and perfected it at the Roman College.

"Do you believe in the Lord in Heaven?" the Buddhist began.

"I do. God Almighty, maker of heaven and earth," said Matteo. "And I ask you the same question: Do you believe in a creator of heaven and earth?"

"Yes, of course, I believe in the Lord of Heaven," replied the Buddhist, "but he is not a greater being than every human."

"If that is the case, then you yourself should be able to create things just as the Lord of Heaven. Do you claim to have such ability?"

"Yes, there is a way in which human beings, including myself, can create heaven and earth," said the Buddhist with confidence.

"Then please, if you will, create for us another pot of food!" said Matteo with laughter.

"That is ridiculous!" said the Buddhist amid the guffaws from the audience of guests. "Now I have a question for you. When you speak of the sun and the moon, do you go into the heavens to look at them or do they come down to you?"

"Neither. I form an image of it in my mind after seeing it with my eyes."

"So you create a new sun and moon?"

"If you see the sun and moon in a mirror, are you foolish enough to think they are the real sun and moon?" countered Matteo.

The debate went on like this for some time and Matteo left feeling the gap of understanding between himself and the Buddhist had only gotten wider.

It was still light outside when he later entered a small public garden with pavilions, rocks, and waterways. He sat on a bench near a pond so that he could watch the lotuses bobbing on the surface. Matteo regretted that he never got the chance to describe even the simplest principles of Christianity at the banquet. He vowed to write a book that would do a better job and would make many copies to give to banquet hosts.

A breeze created ripples across the pond. Matteo reflected on the fact that printed copies of any written work were rare, but they could reach the most learned men of the country. A book that communicated Christianity in a way that all Chinese could understand would be invaluable.

A little girl and boy ran past Matteo along the garden pathway, laughing, with their father fast behind them.

"Give me that stick!" shouted the little boy to his sister.

"No, you have to catch me first," said the girl, who was older and stronger, and seemed to enjoy taunting her little brother.

Matteo watched them run and thought how often he provoked anger in the Chinese, not only for his beliefs but simply for being an outsider. These Chinese were so insulated here in their country. He sighed. As the first person to deliver the message of Christianity here, he might not be the one to convince crowds to convert, but God willing, the Jesuits after him would be able to do so.

Later that evening, he wrote a letter to his friend Girolamo Costa in Rome. "The time of our stay in China is not the time of harvest or even sowing, but of clearing wild forests and fighting with the beasts and poisonous snakes that live in them. Others will come by God's grace and write of conversions and the fervor of the Christians, but it must be known that it was first necessary to do what we are doing now and that we are entitled to most of the merit."

Certainly his mind had been opened too—he now knew more about the Chinese way of thinking than he had ever imagined he would. He understood how important it was to treat everyone with respect. He'd learned about the concept of yin and yang—it was brilliant, simple, profound. And there was so much more he didn't understand.

Under the tutelage of Alessandro Valignano and his other teachers, Matteo maintained humility—he never believed he was superior to anyone. This quality only made him even more of a curiosity to the Chinese.

"Li Madou is a European man from the Western oceans," wrote Gu Qiyuan, a writer who had witnessed the debate between Matteo and the Buddhist. "He has a pale face, a curly beard, and deep-seated eyes the color of bright yellow, like a cat. He knows Chinese. He came to Nanking and resided to the west of Cheng Yang Gate, telling everyone the way of his country is the worship of *Tianzhu*, the Lord of Heaven. This Tianzhu is the creator of heaven and earth. In painting, it is depicted as a little boy held by a woman, called *Tianmu*, heavenly mother."

At the end of a year in Nanking, Matteo and his companions were finally ready to return to Beijing—this time with a plan, and help from Qu Taisu.

Chapter Nineteen

THE TRAP

The more Matteo learned about the eunuchs, the more he feared them.

Castrated servants were employed in the Imperial Palace to guard and protect the emperor's many concubines. They watched over the emperor and had taken over most bureaucratic duties of Beijing—they essentially ran the government.

Was Emperor Wan-li's brain addled from years of taking opium? Matteo considered the evidence and thought it might, indeed, be true. How else could the eunuchs have seized so much power?

These eunuchs—he'd heard there were nearly 20,000 or more—were greedy, lawless, and cruel. Matteo recalled stories about their violence, killing people who got in their way or would not pay the bribes, their extortion of shop owners, their bullying of officials. He also thought of the Chinese people, many of whom lived in abject poverty just outside the walls of the Imperial Palace.

Poor families castrated their young sons and sent them to Beijing hoping that they would be taken into lifelong service at the Imperial Palace. As the number of imperial eunuchs grew, they took over more important jobs, such as collecting taxes and managing businesses. They became gatekeepers to the emperor, reviewing every request for a visit and deciding who would get to see Wan-li and when.

Although from time to time a handful of government officials attempted to overthrow the eunuchs, they were inevitably killed or forced to flee to some far-off province.

Qu Taisu explained all this to Matteo and his Jesuit companions again and again. He wanted them to understand why it would be very difficult and dangerous to try to meet Wan-li. Most of all, he wanted them to be prepared for a possible encounter with the dreaded eunuch Ma Tang.

Bribes would be demanded of them, that was certain. And they needed many gifts for the emperor, which would help get his attention. Matteo sent word for Lazaro Cattaneo to join him and to bring all their treasures—chalices, crucifixes, paintings, maps, the mechanical clock—but to keep them well hidden. He waited eagerly for the young man to arrive.

When Matteo finally laid eyes on his beautiful mechanical clock again, his heart soared. What a masterful instrument! As he stared, he got an idea. He asked Lazaro to find the most talented artist in Nanking to paint the sides of the clock with colorful dragons. A day later, Lazaro located an old man who brought a box filled with paints and began work immediately with great concentration once he heard the request from Matteo.

The results were just what Matteo had wished for—the clock, already impressive, now had the look of a very exotic Chinese item. Matteo thanked the old artist and paid him handsomely. After the paint had completely dried, Matteo carefully wrapped the clock with several layers of thick blankets.

He gathered his books on astronomy, mathematics, and religion and collected all the treasures that he had been saving for just this purpose. Among them were pieces of Venetian glass, painted icons of Jesus and the Virgin Mary, silver crucifixes with inlaid stones, an hourglass, several mirrors, a copy of the New Testament, European coins, and small silver chalices. He wrapped them in tidy bundles in preparation for boarding the junk.

After much consideration, he invited a young Spanish Jesuit named Diego de Pantoja and two Chinese Jesuits who'd taken the names Manuel Pereira and Sebastian Fernandes. They understood the importance of the trip, and all responded with enthusiasm.

It was the spring of a new century, April of the year 1600, when Matteo and his companions said goodbye to Qu Taisu.

"Thank you for being a true and loyal friend," Matteo said, "and for your tremendous guidance. We could not have survived without you."

Qu Taisu's eyes filled with tears. Would he ever see Father Matteo Ricci again? "I only hope that I have prepared you for the challenges ahead, and that you are successful in every way," he said. "I hope to see you again, my friend."

The Jesuits boarded the heavy wooden junk, which belonged to a harmless old eunuch, a merchant who sold silk, and they set off on the now-familiar Grand Canal waterway toward Beijing, watching the figure of Qu Taisu disappear in the distance.

~

As Matteo turned to look out at the passing landscape, he did not feel the thrill of a new adventure. Instead, he was wary and alert. Whenever the boat approached a canal lock, he and the others tensed, fearing that someone would come aboard and try to steal one of their treasures.

After several days, the old eunuch maneuvered the junk into a small inlet.

"Why are you stopping here?" Matteo asked.

"Pay homage," was the blunt reply.

"Pay homage to whom?" Matteo asked.

"You know . . . Ma Tang," said the old man with a shrug, and jumped onto a dirt path that led toward a small, official-looking office building.

Matteo and the three Jesuit men looked at each other in alarm, then hurried below deck, hoping to hide from view.

"Hello, hello!" came a young boy's shout.

Matteo looked out.

"Old man wants me to warn you . . ." the boy looked around quickly. "Ma Tang coming!"

Matteo panicked, but he had no time to escape. Looking down the river path, he saw an entourage of men heading right toward him. He rose and stood on the deck of the junk to meet the men.

As the boy began to run away, Matteo called out to him. "Wait! See if you can find a man called Zhong Wanlu, an official here. He knows me and can help. Now *go!*"

And the boy ran.

When the group reached the Jesuits standing on the deck of the junk, the old man made introductions, avoiding Matteo's eyes.

Ma Tang stepped forward. He was a heavyset man with

large, sleepy eyes and a seemingly permanent half-smile on his face under a drooping mustache. His eyes darted over the junk.

"You're the famous astronomer, yes, I have heard about you. And a religious man too. Now, this old man says you are on your way to the Forbidden City to see the emperor."

"Yes, that is true," replied Matteo in a level tone.

"You must be carrying gifts for the emperor."

"Yes, I am," said Matteo, looking directly into Ma Tang's eyes.

"I would like to see them," said the eunuch.

Matteo stiffened, but when he saw Ma Tang's men step forward with their hands tightening around daggers that hung from their belts, he realized he had no choice.

"Of course, come and see," said Matteo.

Ma Tang followed him below deck and watched as the Jesuit carefully unwrapped a few of the treasures, his eyes widening at the sight of the mechanical clock.

"What is this?"

"It keeps time," said Matteo, not wanting to explain further.

"These are very fine gifts indeed," said Ma Tang with a sarcastic laugh. "So fine, yes, they must be kept safe. Bring them to my boat, which is moored nearby. And I will write a letter to the administration of the Imperial Palace to allow you to visit. Now, you bring these gifts and come with me."

It was a trap. Matteo knew it, but they were far outnumbered and the treasures were heavy. He and his companions grimly wrapped them up and carried them out to the river path, following Ma Tang.

The eunuch's boat, decorated with colorful flags, was large enough to house more than a dozen people. As soon as they stepped onto the boat, Ma Tang's men took the gifts away from the Jesuits and gestured for them to sit and eat. Later they were given a room where they were told to make themselves comfortable.

The next day, Ma Tang summoned Matteo.

"I hope you slept well," said the eunuch with his half-smile that Matteo was beginning to loathe. "I have written the letter, and I will send one of my men to bring it to the palace. I'm sure it will help you. Until we receive a reply, I suggest you and your companions relax. You will be staying here for awhile."

Matteo said nothing. He knew that any letter of introduction to the emperor was to follow a strict protocol or it would be ignored. Had the young boy found Zhong Wanlu, the official he'd met at a banquet in Nanchang?

It might be his only hope.

After a month, Ma Tang ordered Matteo, Diego de Pantoja, Manuel Pereira, and Sebastian Fernandes to be moved to a fortress in the nearby city of Linqing. They were locked in a wing of the fortress with few windows, and given one meal a day. Fearing they would be kept there forever or killed, Matteo and the others began a practice of prayer and meditation throughout each day. Over weeks and months, they grew thinner and their beards longer.

After two months, a guard surprised them by opening the locked door one afternoon. There stood Ma Tang, who was not smiling.

Matteo rose and faced him.

"You didn't tell me . . . you were carrying this," said the eunuch angrily as he thrust forward a large silver cross that had belonged to the Jesuits. "What is this, a man dying? This is bad luck for me."

Matteo began to explain the meaning of the depiction of Christ on the cross, but Ma Tang stopped him.

"And this," he said.

A guard held up a small icon depicting a pale Jesus cradled in the arms of a woman at the base of a wooden cross, blood still dripping from his hands and feet.

"This is not good," said Ma Tang, his mouth set in disapproval.

"This is our holy man," said Matteo, attempting to remain calm at the sight of his beloved treasures. "He suffered because of his beliefs. We worship him and remember his death, and his resurrection."

Ma Tang stared at Matteo in confusion.

"Please, we need these items for our worship," said Matteo. "And the silver chalices, they mean very much to us."

Ma Tang handed the items over to Matteo. He could not wait to get rid of them. "I don't want these things near me," said the eunuch, and turned and left.

Months passed, with no word from Ma Tang or his henchmen about their fate. Matteo feared this was the end for all of them.

Is this my destiny, to die forgotten in a dark fortress? He'd never imagined this. Worst of all, he'd brought the three young Jesuits with him, who would die too. No one would know they were there; no one would know when or how they died. Sebastian grabbed the arm of the guard who brought food and begged him to send word to Zhong Wanlu about their imprisonment. The guard shrugged him off with disgust.

To keep his mind from imagining their death in captivity, Matteo prayed as fervently he had in his early years in Rome—through all waking hours, ceasing only to recite Psalms and passages from the Bible from memory, which calmed them all.

After six months of living as prisoners, the Jesuits were jolted out of their weakened state when one morning a guard opened the door and announced they were to be taken to Ma Tang immediately. The four haggard men walked out into the bright sun, blinking against the unfamiliar light, and marched to Ma Tang's residence.

"Emperor Wan-li has sent word," said Ma Tang, looking at the men with disdain from behind a massive desk. "He wants to see you . . . and he wants all your gifts, especially the one that rings by itself," he said.

Matteo knew instantly that the eunuch was referring to the mechanical clock, and also understood that Ma Tang had no choice but to let them go unharmed. He wondered: *Has Zhong Wanlu learned of our imprisonment and worked to make this new development take place?*

The next day the four Jesuits were reunited with their belongings and guards, and were handed their treasured items with obvious reluctance. The men boarded the large wooden junk as Ma Tang's guards watched their every move.

As the boat left land and eased into the wide river, Matteo caught sight of a boy standing on the riverbank, the very one he'd seen when they first arrived months before. The child waved at them, smiling, and in an instant Matteo realized that the boy had indeed located Zhong Wanlu, who had secured their release from Ma Tang.

The Jesuits crossed themselves and prayed aloud in thanksgiving for their miraculous survival.

Chapter Twenty

RETURN TO BEIJING

As the great walls of Beijing came into view from the junk, Matteo felt a strange mix of dread and excitement. It was a complex and dangerous city, but it represented the ultimate opportunity to him. Here, he must convince the emperor to allow the Jesuits to take up permanent residence and share their Christianity, now and for years to come. The odds were against his success.

As soon as the boat was moored, Matteo and his companions gathered their bags and stepped onto the landing. Almost immediately they were approached by a group of men dressed in dark blue coats who carried daggers at their waists.

"Who are you, foreigners, and what is your purpose?" one of them demanded.

Matteo sized them up and said calmly, "Ma Tang has arranged for us to deliver gifts to the Son of Heaven. They are expecting our arrival at the palace."

His instincts were correct—the men were eunuchs, a few of

the many who roamed the city as self-appointed police. At the mention of Ma Tang's name they visibly drew back and focused their attention on the bundles that the Jesuits carried.

"Ma Tang . . . he sent you?" one asked.

"Yes. By the order he received from the Imperial Palace, we are to bring these gifts immediately," said Matteo.

The eunuchs spoke among themselves for a moment.

"We will escort you."

Three young men pulling carts were commanded to stop and load up the Jesuits and their bags, and the whole group slowly made their way through the crowds toward the Palace.

Suddenly, there it was: the Forbidden City.

The imposing, massive structure dominated the landscape. It was no wonder the Chinese people believed it to be the center of the universe. The buildings were painted a deep purple-red and adorned with gold-and-yellow trim. Its foundation was many layers of bricks topped with thick slabs of marble. Strong cedar columns held up the structures, and thousands of glazed roof tiles could be seen in every direction.

Matteo and his companions stared in awe. Here it was at last—the Imperial Palace, the center of power for all of China. It looked solid enough to withstand wind, storms, and even time, though Matteo had heard that at one time it had been nearly destroyed by fire. Gazing at the massive compound, he had a sinking feeling that his chances of getting in were slim.

The gifts were taken from the carts by the eunuchs and handed over to palace guards, who stood at the entrance holding spears. Matteo presented a long, thick paper made of silk that listed all the gifts, along with an official request for the Jesuits to take up residence in Beijing. The guards studied Matteo carefully, took the message written on the thick paper, then ordered him to a rented house a mile away to await the emperor's response.

Matteo, Sebastian, Diego, and Manuel found the house at the edge of the city and settled in. Days passed as they waited in suspense.

A fantasy plagued Matteo's mind: The emperor, upon seeing the beautiful painted icon of the Jesus and the Madonna, would immediately demand that the missionaries come to live at the palace and teach him everything about their Christian religion, and then ask to be converted. Matteo laughed out loud at his far-fetched dream.

Finally a guard came to their house with urgent news. The emperor liked the mechanical clock, but it had stopped working.

Matteo exchanged looks with his Jesuit brothers. Of course the clock had stopped working—it simply needed to be wound, yet the guards had no way of knowing that. He instantly saw that this gave him leverage.

"Two of you come with me," commanded the guard. "You must make this clock work again or you risk death."

Matteo quickly chose Diego, who knew as much about the clock as he did. They followed the guards back to the palace, their hearts beating fast.

They were escorted through the intimidating palace entrance—with guards watching them closely from atop the corner walls—and walked across a wide, open plaza cut through the middle by a curved moat. Their eyes widened as they crossed one of the five identical marble bridges above the moat and approached the Gate of Supreme Harmony. Two oversized bronze lions with bulging eyes sat on either side of the gate, as if ready to pounce. Inside, Matteo spotted ten men sitting in a circle staring at the mechanical clock in front of them on a low table, as if trying to will it to work again.

One of the eunuchs looked up and motioned for Matteo and Diego to approach.

"Is this the gift that you brought to the Son of Heaven?" he asked accusingly.

Matteo nodded cautiously.

The eunuch continued. "It used to move and ring bells, but it is broken. You fix it, now."

Matteo nodded again and knelt down in front of the clock. "Sir, I will certainly fix this. But I want to teach you and your friends how you can fix it too, so that if it ever stops again, you can please Emperor Wan-li by making it start again."

The eunuchs studied him with great interest.

"It is very easy to learn," said Matteo.

Each of the eunuchs had the same thought: *Knowing how to fix this object that the emperor loved so much would be a great advantage.*

Matteo carefully explained how the spring worked in the clock and demonstrated how to wind it just enough. As the pieces began turning again, the eunuchs murmured appreciatively. The one who seemed to be the leader swiftly picked up the clock and carried it away, while the others stood and accompanied Matteo and Diego back out of the palace.

They were visited again by palace guards a few days later. This time they were asked to explain how to play the small harpsichord that had been given as a gift. Having been trained as a musician, Diego was excited to go with the guards and teach several eunuchs how the instrument was best played, and he offered to return to teach them some European music.

Matteo saw another chance to establish a relationship with

the emperor and his eunuchs: He quickly wrote songs with words that reflected Christian principles, translating them into Mandarin. For several weeks, the eunuchs listened and watched carefully as Diego played the strange instrument and taught them the fundamentals of western music.

While Diego gave these lessons, Matteo and the other Jesuit brothers explored Beijing—they wanted people to become used to seeing them. They were met by the usual stares and yet spoke warmly to anyone who had the courage to greet them.

A guard appeared at the Jesuits' rented house again, this time with a series of questions. The emperor, he said, wanted to know about the people in the countries of Europe.

"What food do they eat, how do they dress, what do they look like?" asked the guard. "And . . . when they die, the Son of Heaven wants to know, what is the ceremony that is held?"

Matteo, Diego, Manuel, and Sebastian each spoke about the customs of Europeans. Matteo described in detail the recent death of Philip II of Spain, and how his coffin was placed in a church. When he was finished with the story, the guard turned and left.

Matteo sensed that this would not be the last time Wan-li would have questions for him. This emperor was a recluse, but he was most certainly curious about the world.

Chapter Twenty-One

MEETING THE EMPEROR

Sporadic visits from the palace guards continued for several months, until at last, one brought astounding news: The emperor wanted to meet Matteo and Diego.

This was unheard of—a privilege that few men were granted.

The two Jesuits immediately put on clean robes and sashes and eagerly accompanied the guard further into the depths of the palace than they had ever been—to the actual living quarters of the emperor and his family. When they were brought into a large room and told to sit, they were excited that finally they would meet the renowned ruler.

Curiously, they noticed that two men wearing dark blue robes who faced easels with paints were also seated in the room. At the sight of Matteo and Diego, the artists began quickly sketching the likenesses of the two Jesuits onto large canvases. Several young women, dressed in colorful silk robes and hiding their faces behind fans, stood behind the artists and giggled intermittently. Matteo assumed they were wives or concubines belonging to the emperor. He could not see their faces, only their eyes, which sparkled with laughter.

After two hours of silent work, the artists stood and said that Matteo and Diego could leave.

Confused, the Jesuits whispered to each other as they left.

"What just happened?" Diego asked.

"I had heard that Wan-li only sees his concubines and his servants. He is protected from all visitors," replied Matteo, "and now I know what that means. Because we are the first Europeans to enter the Forbidden City, he wants to know what we look like. He will now see our portraits, but he may never see us in person."

"What is he afraid of?" asked Diego. "He is surrounded by so many guards, surely we could never hurt him."

"He may be afraid of us for some other reason," said Matteo. "Perhaps he is protecting himself against seeing people who might upset his understanding of the world."

As they returned to their rented house, Matteo and Diego were surprised to see Manuel and Sebastian standing on the street with all their belongings, surrounded by officials.

"They say we must go to a castle where all foreigners stay, until we are granted permission to live here," said Sebastian, looking distressed.

"Don't they understand that we have already given many gifts to the emperor?" Matteo asked angrily, but then stopped himself. The officials and the eunuchs were two different groups, and though Ma Tang had gotten him to Wan-li, he flaunted his power over the local officials, who now wanted to assert their authority too.

"Sebastian, Manuel, Diego—we will go with these officials. Be respectful. We need the help of these men."

The Jesuits nodded and allowed the officials to lead them to a low brick building several miles away.

Upon entering, they were confronted with the smell of sweat and garbage. *Do sheep live here too?* Matteo wondered. They were shown to their rooms, which were simple cells with no doors. The men looked around with dismay. The other tenants were also foreigners, but the Jesuits could barely understand the languages spoken around them. They unpacked their bags and tried as best they could to create livable spaces in the dirty rooms.

Matteo was eager to communicate with these men from far-off countries, and learned that this dilapidated building was called the "foreigners' castle," a security measure for officials to keep track of possible criminals. He discovered that these other tenants came from Tibet, Mongolia, Korea, and other nearby lands. Most of them were merchants who'd brought gems, swords, fabrics, and other gifts for the emperor in hopes of being allowed to do business in Beijing.

He excitedly asked them to calculate the distances they had traveled, about the cities they had seen and waterways they had sailed upon. Matteo took in all this new geographical information, determined to create a revised edition of the map of the world as soon as he was settled.

He knew well the writings of Marco Polo, who described a country he called Cathay. For many years, Europeans had been obsessed with finding it, and now Matteo was convinced without doubt that "Cathay" was actually China.

Yes, he would create a new map and send it to his friends in Rome. That is, if the Jesuits were not expelled from China first.

He smiled to himself when he realized that he'd gotten this

far because of the terrible Ma Tang. Without his intervention, the palace eunuchs would never have allowed him any contact with Wan-li. Yet now he had to contend with the officials who watched his every move in this foreigners' castle.

A few weeks later, a guard pulled Matteo aside to tell him that the emperor wanted him to visit the following day. Was this to be another sitting with the artists who would paint his portrait?

Once again, Matteo and Diego put on their finest robes, which by now were worn and dirty. They were up early and waiting for the guards who came to take them to the emperor.

Once again, they were led through the imposing entrance gate, across the wide courtyard, over the bridge, and up to the Gate of Supreme Harmony. Finally, they were told to enter into a large room with eunuchs standing guard in every corner. In the center of the room was a large golden throne. It was empty.

Matteo and Diego bowed down, their foreheads against the marble floor, and repeated the phrase "ten thousand years," as they had been instructed. Matteo could hear the blood rushing in his ears and the cold odor of the hard floor filled his nostrils. A trickle of sweat ran down his neck as he waited. He sensed the tension in Diego, who remained still in the same bowed position next to him.

When would the emperor enter the room? How long would they have to stay in this awkward, painful position?

Minutes went by, and nothing changed.

Finally Matteo felt a light tap on his shoulder and he and Diego rose. With eyes downcast, they turned to leave. But Matteo could not help but glance quickly at the empty throne in the middle of the room as they left.

His mind was spinning. *Was this presentation of visitors an ancient ritual that they were keeping up even though the current emperor himself never appears? And who benefits from this strange charade?*

Chapter Twenty-Two

A PERMANENT HOME IN BEIJING

As Matteo walked in Zhongshan Park in Beijing, he breathed in the fragrant purple lilacs in glorious bloom. He still could not believe that his wish had been granted.

Wan-li had decreed that the Jesuits could live permanently in Beijing.

Several months after "meeting" the Jesuits in the Forbidden City, the emperor had granted their request, and even offered to give the Jesuits a monthly sum of money to live on. Matteo was now searching Beijing for a permanent residence for the Jesuits, with enough land to build a small chapel nearby.

Permission for the Jesuits to remain in the country's capital had not come by accident. Matteo had employed every ounce of his instinct and diplomatic skills to make sure the officials who governed the foreigners' castle and the eunuchs who controlled the Forbidden Palace were all given small gifts of crystals or globes, and constant assurances that the Jesuits meant no harm.

Matteo had also made it his business to send regular messages to the emperor with intriguing facts about constellations and the orbits of the planets and the phases of the sun and moon, predicting their pathways and positions. He explained why the Venetian glass held up to the sunlight created a rainbow of colors on the ground beneath it. He wrote notes to the emperor about the reason for eclipses, the formation of comets, and the importance of the North Star and planets for sea travel, all of which were embedded in his memory from early lessons in the Roman College from Christopher Clavius.

He received notes back from the emperor, with many questions about astronomy and the instruments Europeans used to track the stars and planets.

In this way, slowly and over weeks and months, Matteo Ricci established a kind of relationship with Wan-li, the emperor of China. Would these exchanges lead to questions about Christianity? He didn't know.

After a few months, a forty-room residence was found, and the Jesuits made it their home in the summer of 1605. They were able to purchase the house with help from a wealthy scholar named Xu Guangqi, who converted to Christianity and became a prominent Chinese Catholic in Beijing.

The house was located near one of the entrances to the Imperial Palace—a strategic advantage, Matteo thought. It was surrounded by a high wall with only one entrance. Next to it, the Jesuits built a long, narrow chapel in which they hung a large portrait of Jesus. An inner courtyard led to rooms where the Jesuits—who now numbered fifteen—slept and ate, as well as a reception hall where Matteo displayed his books and instruments used for astronomy.

In his own room, Matteo hung a painting of the Madonna and Jesus, beside which he placed scrolls with poems he'd written in Chinese about the holy image.

So much has changed since our first visit to Beijing, he thought. *Now, everyone knows we are on favorable terms with the emperor, and they want to know who we are and why we are here.* Matteo shook his head remembering how cold Beijing seemed when he'd come years before. On the street, people still stared at the Jesuits, but at least they did not threaten them or run away in fear.

Just the day before, Sebastian reported that a crowd had actually followed him home, hoping to catch a glimpse of the other Jesuits and their home. Neighbors dropped by often and felt free to ask the Jesuits a thousand questions, which Matteo always welcomed.

One such visitor was a young, well-educated man named Li Zhizao, who had a special interest in geography. He was a lively and curious fellow, who returned again and again to the residence to examine the map and science books, and to discuss matters of geography whenever he could grab Matteo's attention.

Matteo recognized in Li Zhizao a kindred spirit, and was pleased when the young Chinese man offered his help in creating a new version of the map of the world in return for lessons in astronomy. The two collaborated well together—Matteo providing his years of experience and knowledge, and the young man providing energy and focus to complete the task. After that, Li Zhizao wanted to help Matteo translate some of the Jesuit's treasured books, including ones on mathematics, so that Chinese literati could benefit from them.

Li Zhizao reminded Matteo of his old friend Qu Taisu. When Matteo brought up the subject of conversion, the young man declined again and again, until he finally confessed that he did not want to give up his concubine for the sake of Christianity.

This disappointed Matteo, but he was not surprised. The practice of keeping one or more concubines was common among so many men in Beijing, and a significant obstacle in Matteo's efforts to convert them.

By now he was used to such disappointment, though he still spoke of Christian principles to Li Zhizao when he got the chance. Matteo realized he could not dictate how long it would take a man to find the Christian God—he could only offer inspiration.

Matteo had found peace. He enjoyed his new residence, which had quickly become his sanctuary, and even allowed himself to collect several pieces of blue and white Chinese porcelain that he found irresistibly beautiful. "There is nothing like it in European pottery either from the standpoint of the material itself or its thin and fragile construction," he wrote to his brother in Macerata.

Every day he continued to walk the streets of Beijing as best he could, observing the people going about their lives, and seeking potential converts among them. He never discriminated—he spoke to the young and the old, the poor and the rich, the open-minded and the skeptics.

He often explained to his Jesuit brothers that there were many similarities between Christianity and Confucianism, even though the latter was not an organized religion and Confucius was not a holy man, but a philosopher. The five virtues of Confucianism were benevolence, justice, correct ritual, knowledge, and integrity. Surely, he said, no Christian would quarrel that these were good rules to live by.

To the young men who did convert to Christianity, Matteo

gave his most focused attention. He dearly wished that he had more written texts to share with them, ones they could hold and study to deepen their understanding.

His latest accomplishment was finally finishing a book he had been writing for ten years, which he called *True Meaning of the Lord of Heaven*. He'd written it as a dialogue that he intended to use as a catechesis for the literati. He hoped it was as lively as debates he'd had with scholars when he spelled out to them the principles of Christianity and heard them describe Confucianism. He made a point not to denigrate any beliefs of the Chinese. "I do nothing but speak of virtue and living a good life in a very complete way as a natural philosopher, but also as a Christian without refuting any sect," he wrote to his friends in Rome. Soon after the book was first printed in Beijing, copies were in high demand and it became a much sought-after item.

Matteo hoped *True Meaning of the Lord of Heaven* would allow the Chinese to better understand Christianity and see similarities to their own beliefs. He also hoped the book would show his friends in Rome the challenges he faced as a missionary in this foreign land of "unbelievers," as he called them. *Do they have any idea what our life is like here?* Matteo often wondered.

He never knew if his letters reached their destinations, but he wrote regularly to General Acquaviva, to Alessandro Valignano, and to his former classmates at the Roman College, now scattered all over the world. To Fabio de Fabii, who had succeeded Alessandro as novice master at the Roman College, Matteo wrote asking for prayers for the China missionaries, adding "Your graciousness is remembered with particular affection by one of your poor brothers, thrust to the end of the world among infidels."

The profound alienation of living in Asia, so far away from

everything that was familiar—language, food, religion, government—was difficult to express to his friends and family in Italy.

"We, the religious, are in these countries like in a voluntary exile," he wrote to his brother in Macerata, "not only far away from our dear ones, father, mother, brothers, and relatives, but also from Christians and our nation, and sometimes in places where in ten or twenty years one does not see a single European, and others, such as those who are in China, never eat bread nor drink wine . . . We are here with our long beards and hair down to our backs."

As the men prayed silently together one evening, Matteo suddenly felt the need for the physical touch of the sacred texts that were found in the chapels in Rome, Lisbon, and Goa, India. How he had taken them for granted when he was younger! Now he sorely felt their absence, as a Christian and as a missionary. In a community of Christian faith, the Bible was at the center, through which God's nature was revealed.

Matteo had heard of a Bible made by Christopher Plantin in Belgium, in which the Old and New Testaments were printed in five languages—Hebrew, Greek, Latin, Syriac, and Aramaic—along with ornate frontispieces and historiated initials. Surely a treasure such as this—a rare and beautifully created edition of the sacred texts—would move the hearts of the recently converted young men.

The next morning, Matteo sent a letter to Rome asking if it would be possible for one of the few Plantin Bibles to be sent to Beijing for his China mission. It was a bold request.

The answer finally came six months later: the Plantin Bible was on its way.

Now, he simply had to employ two skills he had learned so well in China: faith and patience.

Chapter Twenty-Three

MIRACULOUS ARRIVAL

Cold rain pelted down from heavy, dark clouds over Beijing. It had been raining for weeks that summer, and the air was thick and humid. Some of the rivers in northern China had overflowed, sweeping away entire houses along the banks.

Father Gaspar Ferreira had been given the task of delivering the Plantin Bible to Matteo in 1604, and now he was on a boat moving swiftly along the Grand Canal. He held tightly to the side of the junk, which carried cases of food and wine and precious bundles of tightly packed burlap. The Grand Canal had risen higher than anyone could remember, and though Gaspar was within an hour of his final destination, his heart was beating fast—these surging waves and rocky canal banks could easily capsize the little boat. The boatmen shouted to each other over the roar of rain and the rushing water, but Gaspar could not make out their words.

He leaned over the edge of the boat, straining to catch a glimpse of the landing point. Then, suddenly, he spotted an unmistakable tall figure: Father Matteo Ricci himself was standing on a small dock with another man, scanning the river. Yes, that was his long beard and cassock—it was him!

Gaspar stood up and waved his arms in excitement. At last he would deliver the treasured volumes of the Plantin Bible to this brave and famous missionary.

When Matteo caught sight of the boat through the downpour, he too began to wave.

At that very instant, the junk hit a rock, and with a violent jolt Gaspar was thrown back. His head hit the hard wooden deck just as the boat began to splinter. He reached for the bundle, but his vision went blurry, and then he blacked out.

From the shore, Matteo and Sebastian watched in horror as the boat came apart, large pieces of wood shooting off into the brown currents. Gaspar's limp body tumbled into the muddy waves, and cases of wine that had been intended for their Mass services slid heavily into the water too. Soon after, the burlap bundles rolled into the water.

Matteo and Sebastian raced along the slippery bank of the canal, shouting for help. Peasants came running with long sticks and rope to save the men.

Matteo reached Gaspar first. He waded into the deep water to pull the unconscious man to shore with the help of villagers. But Sebastian had his eyes on the burlap bundles. Two men in a nearby boat had scooped them up with their fishing nets. Pulling their boat to the shoreline, the men stopped to rip open the tight wrapping. They looked down in confusion at the strange writing, some of it gold, on heavy pages of paper.

Sebastian approached the men carefully, unable to hide his anguish at seeing the papers exposed to hard-driving rain.

"Hello!" he shouted to get their attention. "That belongs to my friend who nearly drowned just now from the boat. Please give the boxes to me—they are very important."

The two men now grew interested, and pulled the boxes closer to them while scrutinizing Sebastian, trying to figure out his intent.

"It's just a lot of paper . . . here, I will give you money if you just give the boxes to me . . . what value could they be for you?" He stood before them, the rain pouring down his face and outstretched hand. When they were silent, he dug into his satchel and pulled out some copper coins.

"There you see, please take these. Just give me the boxes."

One man got out of the boat and walked over to Sebastian, reaching out to take the coins. But Sebastian withdrew them.

"The boxes must be placed here now, then I will give you the coins."

They did as he asked, and he dropped the money in their hands. Sebastian quickly pulled off his frock and covered the boxes, then picked them up and hurried to Matteo, who was tending to Gaspar.

"Go, now—take them to the house," said Matteo when he looked up. "I will bring Father Ferreira there as soon as we can carry him."

Was it rain or was it tears that coursed down Matteo's face as he spoke gently to Gaspar? The man was now regaining consciousness. Holding his head, which was bleeding profusely, he whispered, "Father Ricci . . . the Bible!"

"We have it, fear not," said Matteo. "Now, see if you can walk and we'll get you to some dry clothes and food!"

Incredibly, Gaspar had transported the Bible a distance of more than 1,200 miles, from Macao up the coast to Beijing. Yet that was just the last leg of the Bible's long journey. It had been donated to the China mission by a cardinal in Rome, and was delivered to the Jesuit missionaries in Macao the year before, in 1604.

Within a few months, most Beijing residents had heard about the sacred book of the Christians and its miraculous arrival. Matteo put it on display for visitors to see, though he stood by it to make sure no one got too close. The large pearl-white pages, fresh and bright, almost seemed to glow.

Its beauty is unlike anything they have ever seen, thought Matteo as he watched the Chinese visitors gaze in awe at the elegant book.

Matteo believed that it was nothing less than a miracle that the Bible had survived its journey halfway around the world. It was common for letters to be lost or arrive to their recipients years after being sent. This Bible would be critical to his missionary work. Too many men who had converted to Christianity drifted away after a year or so. Matteo knew that the Bible—tangible evidence of the word of God—would capture the spiritual imagination of followers.

To be able to touch these texts—this too was a miracle. And surely, he thought, the Bible would bring many more miracles.

Chapter Twenty-Four

A NEW LIFE

M atteo was deeply grateful to Father Gaspar Ferreira and invited him to stay at their residence in Beijing as long as he wanted.

Father Alessandro Valignano had gladly contributed funds for the purchase of the Beijing house, the building of the chapel, and the digging of a well. He suffered from kidney problems, but his support for missionary work never wavered. He was intensely proud of Father Matteo Ricci and all that he had accomplished. Though ill, Alessandro longed to visit China—he wanted to see for himself the Jesuit residences in Shaozhou, Nanking, Nanchang, and, of course, Beijing.

But he never got the chance. Alessandro Valignano died in January of 1606 at age sixty-six, just as his Jesuit brothers were making his travel preparations.

"His death was felt and wept over by the Fathers of the two Christian missions in Japan and China," wrote Matteo to his friends in Rome. Alessandro had been a brave missionary whose vision of befriending the Chinese and Japanese people rather than forcing Christian beliefs upon them was radically new.

As Matteo walked in his garden, deep in contemplation, he prayed for Alessandro's soul and was grateful that his former mentor was finally with God. He smiled remembering the first time he showed up unannounced to meet this revered mentor and teacher. Matteo had been a rash young man, wildly pursuing his romantic idea of becoming a missionary. Alessandro, who had once been very much the same, recognized a true missionary spirit. He allowed Matteo to enter the Society of Jesus in Rome, where Matteo felt his real life had begun.

When Matteo returned to the house, he found a letter had been delivered for him—it was from his old friend Qu Taisu. In it he announced that he had decided at last to marry his concubine and convert to Catholicism. Matteo smiled at this news and his heart leapt with joy. How many years had he prayed for this? True to Alessandro's teaching, Matteo had never tried to force Qu Taisu to convert, though his friend was already Christian in almost every way.

The news was gratifying. The Jesuits had converted more than one hundred Beijing residents since arriving—and many were of the elite class of the city. They celebrated feast days and at Christmas they held Masses that featured harpsichord music and Latin prayers. They fasted together at Lent. Some claimed to have visions and dreams of the Virgin Mary and God.

This was the fruit of many years of hard work and loss. Matteo remembered each of his devoted friends who'd supported his mission in China.

Michele Ruggieri, joyous and fun, had recently died in Salerno.

Lazaro Cattaneo, a devoted friend whose first concern was

always Matteo's health, had moved back to Macao after living for many years in the Shaozhou residence.

The enthusiastic Chinese Jesuit Francisco Martins, with a heart of a child, was captured and tortured after he was falsely accused of plotting an invasion, and died in prison.

And more recently Li Zhizao, the intelligent young Chinese man who had helped Matteo translate so many significant books, had recently decided to marry his concubine and convert—another miracle!

And the Confucian-turned-Christian scholar named Xu Guangqi had helped Matteo with the Chinese translation of *Elements of Geometry* by Euclid and other scientific books, which increased the fame and reach of the Jesuits' reputation.

How grateful I am for all of them, thought Matteo. It was time to write a history of the China mission—Matteo was determined that the world should remember every challenge and success.

For the first time since he had left Rome, he realized that his melancholy had truly lifted. He was deeply happy. "I am old and tired," he wrote to a friend in Rome the year before he died, "but healthy and strong, praise be to the Lord!"

In his fifth decade, the Jesuit no longer traveled outside of Beijing. He was left alone by the powerful eunuchs because Emperor Wan-li now treated him as privileged astronomer-mathematician-in-residence. At one point, he asked Matteo to make copies of his map of the world. *Has he seen this map or has someone told him of its existence?* Matteo wasn't sure, but he created two new maps with Chinese notations for Emperor Wan-li so that they could be hung on either side of the throne.

Matteo really had no need to leave the city. It was difficult for him to walk—the old ankle injury from the attack in Zhaoqing had never completely healed. His daily routine included prayer, leading services, giving lessons to new converts, and teaching mathematics. And of course, the Jesuits continued to receive many visitors every day. The first knock on the door usually came during breakfast, causing the young priests to groan.

Matteo stopped them. "Even though it is a lot of hard work, let everyone be welcomed here," he admonished, "for the good wishes of all as well as the possibility of talking to them about the matters of our faith."

Whenever possible, he also diligently made the rounds of visits to local officials and educated men, always seeking people who were interested in converting. He always tried to use the fascination of others toward him as a way to begin discussing spiritual matters.

"One of the most time-consuming occupations I have here is to respond in Chinese to the continuous stream of letters that come in from different parts of the country, from very important people," he wrote to General Adolfo Acquaviva in Rome, "all who want to contact me because of my fame."

Every encounter, and every letter, was an opportunity for evangelism.

Chapter Twenty-Five

FINAL DAYS

Matteo worried that his life might soon come to an end—he suffered headaches that suddenly seemed to be worse. He started to make arrangements for the Jesuits to buy land for the burial of Jesuit priests.

On May 3, 1610, exhausted from the uninterrupted arrival of visitors to the Jesuit residence, Matteo asked that his bed be moved to the ground floor. Soon after, he became weak and unable to rise. Li Zhizao brought in his own physician, but no medicine seemed to help. The Jesuit brothers panicked at the thought of losing their leader and stayed in Matteo's room, praying continually.

A few days later, Matteo made his confession and took communion. Then he fell into a delirious state, frightening his Jesuit companions.

Li Zhizao and Xu Guangqi sat closest to Matteo's bed, each man holding one of his hands. They spoke comforting words to him, not knowing if he was awake or asleep.

"Father, you have brought the word of God to people who need it very much," said the young Li Zhizao, barely holding back tears. "Be assured, we will continue your work here. Everything you have begun will continue forever."

Matteo's eyes were closed but he squeezed Li Zhizao's hand.

"You have accomplished many great things," said Xu Guangqi, the scholar. "Your work is known and admired, and many will follow in your footsteps, as you have followed in the footsteps of your beloved Francis Xavier."

A small smile crossed Matteo's face at these words. Suddenly he opened his eyes.

"My brothers, remember to welcome new priests who come to China with kindness. I give you my blessing." Matteo collapsed back into his pillow.

The next day, May 10, 1610, at age fifty-seven, Father Matteo Ricci died.

Word quickly spread of the death of the famous Jesuit who dressed like a Confucian scholar. As Matteo would have wanted, the Jesuits opened their doors and allowed Chinese visitors to pour in to mourn the man they knew as Li Madou, who had lived among them in peace for so many years. The priests, wearing white robes according to the Chinese custom, stood in the room next to Matteo's body, watching as each guest entered and bowed four times.

Emperor Wan-li sent a message to the Jesuits, granting approval for Matteo to be buried in a plot of land in Beijing. A large villa with many gardens was found, and a chapel was built next to it. Matteo Ricci's tomb was placed at the center.

Epilogue

From 1601 until his death in 1610, Matteo Ricci never left Beijing, where he lived in comfort and peace.

Though he was discouraged by the initial Chinese reactions of fear and suspicion toward him, Matteo succeeded in opening the minds of many Chinese people of the Ming dynasty to Christianity, to scientific knowledge, and to the larger world. And he proved that conversion to Christianity was more enduring when people were shown the ways in which it was similar to their own ancient traditions and beliefs.

Matteo remained frustrated that in his twenty-seven years in China he had not made more than several hundred converts. Yet his vast knowledge in astronomy and mathematics convinced China's Emperor Wan-li to allow Jesuits to remain in China, which made it possible for them to live there for centuries to come, and to continue the missionary work that Matteo started.

About the Author

Nicole is a writer and editor living in Southern California with her husband and son. She has written for the *Boston Globe, Los Angeles* magazine, the *Los Angeles Times*, the *Orange County Register*, and other publications, and has edited a number of books. She particularly enjoys writing profiles of unknown people. In her free time she likes to travel, cook, and read fiction.

NOW AVAILABLE FROM THE MENTORIS PROJECT

America's Forgotten Founding Father
A Novel Based on the Life of Filippo Mazzei
by Rosanne Welch, PhD

A. P. Giannini—The People's Banker
by Francesca Valente

A Boxing Trainer's Journey
A Novel Based on the Life of Angelo Dundee
by Jonathan Brown

Building Heaven's Ceiling
A Novel Based on the Life of Filippo Brunelleschi
by Joe Cline

Building Wealth
From Shoeshine Boy to Real Estate Magnate
by Robert Barbera

Christopher Columbus: His Life and Discoveries
by Mario Di Giovanni

The Divine Proportions of Luca Pacioli
A Novel Based on the Life of Luca Pacioli
by W. A. W. Parker

Dreams of Discovery
A Novel Based on the Life of the Explorer John Cabot
by Jule Selbo

The Faithful
A Novel Based on the Life of Giuseppe Verdi
by Collin Mitchell

Fermi's Gifts
A Novel Based on the Life of Enrico Fermi
by Kate Fuglei

First Among Equals
A Novel Based on the Life of Cosimo de' Medici
by Francesco Massaccesi

God's Messenger
The Astounding Achievements of Mother Cabrini
A Novel Based on the Life of Mother Frances X. Cabrini
by Nicole Gregory

Grace Notes
A Novel Based on the Life of Henry Mancini
by Stacia Raymond

Harvesting the American Dream
A Novel Based on the Life of Ernest Gallo
by Karen Richardson

Soldier, Diplomat, Archaeologist
A Novel Based on the Bold Life of Louis Palma di Cesnola
by Peg A. Lamphier, PhD

The Soul of a Child
A Novel Based on the Life of Maria Montessori
by Kate Fuglei

FUTURE TITLES FROM THE MENTORIS PROJECT

A Biography about Alessandro Volta
A Biography about Rita Levi-Montalcini
and
Novels Based on the Lives of:
Amerigo Vespucci
Andrea Doria
Andrea Palladio
Antonin Scalia
Antonio Meucci
Artemisia Gentileschi
Buzzie Bavasi
Cesare Becaria
Father Eusebio Francisco Kino
Federico Fellini
Frank Capra
Galileo Galilei
Giuseppe Garibaldi
Guido d'Arezzo
Harry Warren
Laura Bassi
Leonardo Fibonacci
Maria Gaetana Agnesi
Mario Andretti
Peter Rodino
Pietro Belluschi
Saint Augustine of Hippo
Saint Francis of Assisi

For more information on these titles and
the Mentoris Project, please visit
www.mentorisproject.org

Made in the USA
San Bernardino, CA
26 January 2020